DATE DUE

OCT 0 4 2006	

DEMCO, INC. 38-2931

A Gift For

_____

~ From ~

_____

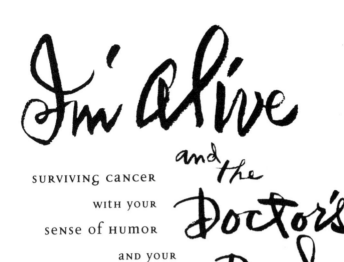

I'm alive and the Doctor's Dead

SURVIVING CANCER
WITH YOUR
SENSE OF HUMOR
AND YOUR
SEXUALITY INTACT

Formerly titled *Love, Laughter, and a High Disregard for Statistics*

Sue Buchanan

Hallmark BOOKS ■ Zondervan

BOK3020

99 00 01 02 03 04 /❖ DC/ 10 9 8 7 6 5 4 3 2

To Wayne, of course

Contents

Acknowledgments

THANK YOU!

My family: Wayne, the good guy in the book who was my greatest support; Dana, who was always available to talk things over; Mindy Buchanan, Barry Shafer, Becky, Cara, and Kirby Davis; Jon Davis, my brother, who helped me with things related to the computer. I'm thanking him although he hasn't always been kind. He said the length of my fingernails rendered me useless to society.

Joy MacKenzie, Peggy Benson, and Gloria Gaither, my "friends through thick and thin."

Author Jerry Jenkins, who said, "You can write this book!" then cheered me each step of the way and put me in touch with his literary agent Rick Christian.

Rick Christian and Greg Johnson at Alive Communications.

Ann Spangler who is not only a great editor, but is fun to work with.

Rose Ann Miller, my "authority" on most medical issues. One weekend she let me use her summer home in the woods where I did some of my most intense writing (and fishing).

Larry Stone, Murray and Donna Fisher, Joy Williams, Bonnie Shafer, The Hipple Cancer Institute, Dr. Martin J. Murphy, Jr., Dr. Ralph Parchment, Dr. Connie Erickson-Miller, Dr. Alan Winfield, Dr. Marvin Burnett and staff, and Kate Rupert.

My Sunday night group, who loves and encourages me, prays for me, and laughs with me: Jimmy Hodges, Lynn Hodges, Bob MacKenzie, Joy MacKenzie, Nancy Guthrie, David Guthrie, Evelyn Allen, John Yarborough, Betsy Yarborough, Marsha Blackburn, Chuck Blackburn, Matt Baugher, Debbie Baugher, Sarah Brewer, Will Brewer, Jean Davis, and Bill Davis.

And finally, my cats—Jazz and Dizz.

Introduction

THERE'S NOTHING I HATE more than waiting an unreasonable amount of time for a doctor. I resent the fact that he thinks his time is more important than mine, not to mention that he insults me with his six-month-old magazines. Though I'm not proud of this, I always have the urge to get him back.

Once when my girls were little and we had to wait a ridiculous amount of time, we took the doctor's tongue depressors out of his big jar, drew little people pictures on them, stuck cotton balls on their heads for hair, and lined them up all around the room. We never had to wait for him again!

Another time, after a long wait, I took the doctor's diplomas down from the wall and hung them back up—upside down. Never had to wait for him again, either!

The third time I tried to play havoc with a doctor's life, it backfired. Again it was a long wait; again I became impatient—downright bored—and this time, I began looking through all the stuff on my doctor's desk. Yes, this was a bad thing to do, but I simply couldn't help myself. I was bored! In my rummaging, however, I uncovered a file folder with my name on it. I opened it and discovered a letter he had written to an associate. His prediction was that I would be dead before the year was out—not those exact words, but I got the picture. To say I was taken aback is an understatement. Shaking like a leaf, I broke out in a cold sweat, followed by a hot flash, and back to a cold sweat. Then I noticed the letter had been written ten months earlier and I only had to live two more months to prove him wrong. That's when the ol' "I'll show him" mode kicked in.

That was fifteen years ago and here I am! *I'm alive and the doctor's dead.* It's absolutely true, but when I say it in the presence of my daughter Dana, she says, "Mo-*ther*! Don't say that. It sounds mean-spirited." Dana will not approve of the title of this book, but let me explain to her and to you that it's not intended to be mean-spirited. It's intended to bring hope to those who have been given the death sentence, either by a doctor or from the statistical "evidence" they've uncovered on their own. In my daughter Dana's case, it was a friend, a doctor's daughter, who boldly pronounced, "Your mother is as good as dead!"

This book is here to say ignore the naysayers, ignore the statistics. The computer doesn't know you. It doesn't know how often you laugh or cry or that you have spunk. It doesn't know about the support of your family and friends and how well you're loved; whether or not you're prayed for isn't taken into consideration by the statisticians. And no matter how many mega-giga-*humonga*-bytes-bits-RAM the computer may contain, it simply isn't capable of computing the fact that—are you ready for this?—*the God of the universe has a timetable for your life and mine!* Yea! Rah! Cheers! Maybe a hallelujah or two!

This book is also here to say enjoy the moment. One evening not long ago, I was batting it down the highway—in a hurry for no reason at all—when I noticed that, in spite of the fact the sun was shining brightly, it had begun to rain. I slowed down a bit and did a quick scan of the sky, thinking conditions were right for a rainbow. I wasn't disappointed! There to my left was not one rainbow, but *two*. A double rainbow that encompassed the entire horizon! I slowed down and pulled to the side of the road, overcome by the spectacular view. It wasn't long until another car pulled in behind me. Then another. Then another. Four of us, all hanging out our car windows, smiling and pointing skyward. As I drove away, it occurred to me that they, like me, had probably survived something, had been given a second chance at life, and were appreciating it to the fullest.

Perhaps only those who have faced a life-threatening experience (or gone through it with a loved one) can fully understand when I say that, before my illness, I might have missed the awe of that moment. I certainly would not have been able to fathom pulling off the road just to soak it in. But having cancer changed my life. Life is more precious. I appreciate simple things and an *I-don't-want-to-miss-anything* perspective prevails. I'm on the lookout for double rainbows.

I wish I could say I'm a better person. In some ways I am, but when it comes to doctors, I still do unruly things when I have to wait too long. Not long ago, I went to the doctor because of an ear infection; while I was waiting in the examining room, I discovered a humongous roach lying dead behind a chair. I couldn't resist! I picked it up, laid it on its back on the table—legs pointing heavenward—pulled out my trusty magic marker, drew a circle around it, and wrote in large letters: *Here lies the body of the doctor's last patient. Lie down here at your own risk.*

Life is fun. Life is precious. Cherish the moments and look for the rainbows. As for statistics, it's all just fairy dust.

Red and Pink and Purple

My HUSBAND CLIMBED INTO my hospital bed with me. His arm went around my shoulder as his free hand stroked my face and neck. He caressed my arm and traced the veins in my wrist and then each finger. As his dear, familiar hands roamed my body he carefully avoided the place he usually touched first: my breasts. Breasts big enough to evoke teasing from my close friends.

Years earlier, my friend Peggy's four-year-old son Patrick, who is the same age as my Mindy, had climbed on my lap, looked me over, and said, "You sure do have bosoms!" A few days later my husband, Wayne, and I joined Peggy and her husband, Bob, for dinner. As we got out of our respective cars in the parking lot of Jimmy Kelly's restaurant, the two of them shouted in unison, "You sure do have bosoms!" I cringed and glanced around, hoping no one heard. My family had never joked about such things. In fact as I was growing up, my father referred to my bra as "that undergarment you wear." Wayne and I had recently moved to Nashville from a rather stuffy community in the north where breasts or bosoms, for that matter, weren't discussed in public. At least not in our circle of friends.

Everybody in the parking lot of Kelly's heard, including the doorman, the valet, and an elderly couple getting out of a cab, and *everyone* was laughing. I felt embarrassed but managed a tenuous smile, hoping to show what a good sport I was. The next thing I knew, I had wholeheartedly joined them and my husband in their belly laughs. For the first time in my life, I was laughing at my top-heavy figure. We all laughed just as hard on another night, in another restaurant, when Bob looked in the direction of my chest and said, "You seem tired; sit down and get a load off your feet!"

Not only could we tease about my breasts, but as our friendship developed, so did our ability to find more opportunities to joke about each other's flaws. "Distinguishing characteristics," we called them. When we went swimming, we laughed about Bob's puny body and the one, lonesome hair on his chest. There was always a good-natured dig at my husband's weight problem: "Pull up a couple of chairs and sit down!" In the same manner, we joked about Peggy's "Bugs Bunny" teeth. The fact that her teeth protrude is one of the reasons she is so cute, in my opinion. They were, and are, such a vital part of her. So very *Peggy*. Likewise, even though I was embarrassed by the size of them, I realized my breasts were an essential element of my *Sue*ness. They were the essence of my equilibrium and balance and of my lovemaking. One caress made my heart pound and my body tingle.

That was before the operation. Now there was nothing to touch but a bandage six inches thick, which encased my upper torso like a mummy. It was so thick, I had nothing to wear over it, only the ugly hospital gown designed to fit any physique, male or female, fat or thin, tall or short—or someone with only one breast.

Looking down at the faded unibody rag, my heart ached as I thought of never again being able to wear the silky, low-cut gowns I loved so much. I was pained to think how this would affect my husband who, in our first year of marriage, jokingly threatened to throw me on the floor if I ever came to bed in one of *those* flannel nightgowns. Even though he was joking, I remembered how distastefully he spat out the words, much the way he would describe "one of *those* wretched sopranos" or "one of *those* dreadful little barking dogs." Lying there in the hospital, I was sure I'd never again enjoy doing what felt so very good: crawling between the sheets and feeling the pleasurable closeness of skin against skin.

That's exactly what I was thinking. Not about cancer or what I might face as a result of this awful disease: months of sickening chemotherapy, burns from radiation, the loss of my hair or maybe even my eyebrows and fingernails. The possibility of dying at the hands of this cruel killer never even crossed my mind. I was only dealing with the unsightly loss of my breast, a part of my body that had been important to me since I was thirteen.

Maybe it was because I grew up during the Marilyn Monroe era. Whatever the reason, breasts were on everyone's mind at Charleston, West Virginia's Woodrow Wilson Junior High School in 1948. Boys whispered about them and girls wanted them. Even then we sensed they were symbols of our femininity. Our primary concerns were, "When will I have them?" "How big will they be?" and "Will it happen overnight?"

The questions were answered one morning when I woke up, turned over on my stomach in bed, and had the strangest feeling I'd rolled on top of the cat. Since I didn't hear the prerequisite "Mrr-ye-ow!" I reached down to feel what other obtrusion might be present and was profoundly surprised to discover it was me— two mounds of me that weren't there before. One day I was flat as a pancake; the next, my mother hustled me off to Stone and Thomas Department Store where I was fitted (in those days it was almost like being fitted for shoes) in a bra—*size 32B!* Some kids skipped a grade in school. I skipped an A cup.

The day we purchased bras, my mother bought me a hunter green sweater and color-coordinated plaid skirt. Giggling as I stood sideways admiring myself in the mirror, I decided I looked pretty good and pretty grown-up too. The next day, in my new outfit, I gave a campaign speech to my seventh-grade class, stating my promises if elected class president. Afterward, as I made my way to the back of the auditorium, I saw Darryl Riley take a quick glance around to see if anyone was watching. Then he stepped toward my brand new anatomy with both hands open and a wicked look in his seventh-grader eyes, and proceeded to give me the quickest squeeze in history. From that moment on, I had mixed feelings about having breasts.

In junior high school, most girls—if they had breasts at all—had compact, pert little breasts. Not me! I soon graduated from a B to a C cup, which was not at all becoming on my otherwise undeveloped, straight-as-a-stick figure. No one had breasts the size of mine, not even the teachers. My endowment was sheer torture on my young, peer-pressured psyche, and I would have swapped for a set of compact little breasts in an instant.

In gym class I thought of myself as a freak in the institutional, one-piece, blue cotton uniform we had to wear. The outfit was baggy over my shapeless hips and the elastic kept losing its grip on what was supposed to be the wide part of my toothpick legs. The biggest problem was the top. It stretched tightly over my chest and gaped wide between snaps. My breasts bounced right along with the basketball and felt sore for hours afterward.

Nothing was worse, though, than taking a shower at the end of class. It was the rule: Strip naked and be monitored under the full force of the water. The girls who did the monitoring were invariably the teacher's pets, cheerleader-types with tan bodies and—you guessed it—compact, pert little breasts! Overwhelmed with insecurities, I *died* each time I was forced to undress and parade through the shower.

By the time I went to college I was a 32 Double D, once again skipping a cup size, but I'd come to think of my top-heavy figure as acceptable—even pleasing—to me, as well as to others. I remember one spring night, a group of the guys sat at the foot of the stairway in the girls' dorm, and as we came down to dinner, they whispered and laughed and looked us over from head to toe. We, of course, wanted in on their secret, so we questioned, only to discover they were assembling the "perfect woman" from our various body parts. This was before the women's movement, light-years before any of us could spell or even define the word *chauvinist*.

We kept prying and then laughed along when we found out the ideal body consisted of Marge Sweet's angelic face, Marjorie Johnson's thick shining hair, JayCee Matt's cute shapely legs, Janice Woodring's backside, and my front side.

Although no one said the word "breasts" aloud in those days, they beat around the bush with enough "Sue's—*you know!*" that any fool could figure out what part of *me* completed their jigsaw puzzle of perfection.

Now one of those "perfect" breasts was gone forever. On the sixth floor of the hospital in Nashville, Tennessee, my husband and I were alone. Visitors had been coming and going all day, but it was quiet for the moment. Wayne hadn't left my side: fluffing my pillows, holding the straw while I sipped water, stewing about too many visitors, and making jokes when the conversation became overly serious.

As we lay there, our bodies pressed together, Wayne reminded me that he'd taken care of me for almost twenty-five years and assured me that he would continue to do that, no matter what. However, as I watched him watching me, I wondered if those were just empty words to make me feel better. He said he'd love me, this man who had so wholeheartedly enjoyed my breasts, but how could I be so sure he'd love just half of me?

Wayne and I have always loved each other, but there were times we didn't much *like* each other, and a couple of times we thought we couldn't go on. During the downs, I often quoted my father: "Okay, now, let's just snap out of it!" or "We've mully-grubbed long enough now!" or "It's time to bounce back!"

Years before in a dark, despairing moment, I had stood on the balcony of a hotel, high above Philadelphia, and fought a compelling urge to jump, to end my feeling of utter desolation. I knew I was high enough to ensure a fatal fall, but fortunately I reasoned that my two daughters couldn't make it without a mother or survive the stigma of such an act. Eventually, my husband loved me back from the edge.

Many years after that Wayne wrote me a letter during a bad time, saying why we *should not* divorce. He listed such things as forsaken dreams and memories, the hurt it would bring our daughters, the regrets we'd harbor, and then he reassured me of his love despite our conflicts. "Love is strong enough to get us through," he wrote.

Could he offer the same reassurance now that my body was repulsive. Could he once again love me back from the edge of despair? Perhaps equally important, would I give him the chance?

Silently we lay—side by side in each other's arms—engulfed in our own private thoughts. Above our heads hung twelve helium-filled balloons in various shades of red and pink and purple. Trailing from them, just low enough to touch, were the ribbons, the kind that crinkle and curl when scraped with scissors, the kind my mother-in-law, Mom Buchanan, used to tie up her packages. As Wayne and I finally began to talk about the events that brought us to this moment, we fingered the ribbons, pulling a balloon toward us and letting go, pulling and letting go. We watched it bounce against the ceiling, just as our emotions, and even our prayers, seemed to be doing. One thing was obvious: the balloons had far more resiliency than we did at that moment, maybe more than we could ever hope for again.

Tomorrow Is Just a Day Away

I DON'T REMEMBER WHEN I found the lump. In fact, there never really was a lump, just a thickening in the lower left quadrant of my left breast. When I was in the tub and my fingers were soapy, I felt it. Then later, feeling nothing, I could talk myself out of the possibility.

Long before I was even able to feel the thickening, I had begun to have a hurting. Actually, it was more like a heaviness, an uneasiness in my breast. I tried to put it out of my mind, but the feeling nagged me, like the memory of a nightmare. Neither could I ignore magazine articles that told me my chances of having breast cancer were considerably higher than normal because the disease ran in my family. The odds were against me: Mother had recently had a mastectomy.

Terrified by the grim statistics, I finally called my gynecologist's office. The receptionist sensed the urgency in my voice as I described my problem and scheduled an appointment that very afternoon. Within hours, I was in the examination room slipping into a white, sterile-smelling cotton gown.

"Put the opening toward the front, just opposite what you would think," the tall, gray-haired nurse instructed. As I climbed onto the examining table, I glanced at the stirrups and took comfort in knowing that today at least, I'd be spared that particular contortion. I fanned through an outdated, dog-eared magazine (the only kind doctors ever stock) I'd picked up in the waiting room. I couldn't concentrate.

My stomach felt queasy. I glanced at my watch. Then my eyes followed the straight line of pictures around the perimeter of the room. Ducks, perfect ducks, all headed in the same direction, all nearly identical, all framed alike in narrow black frames with gray linen mats. "Quack doctor's office," I muttered to myself, unable to fathom why anyone would want so many ducks that looked so alike. I could only hope the doctor would consider me as a unique individual, different from the long line of patients who had preceded and would follow me, each with distinct needs and concerns.

If I had to wait much longer, I'd amuse myself by making his tongue depressors into little people. My children and I had done that very thing years ago while waiting for our pediatrician. What do you do with two little girls stripped down to their panties who know the doctor has decided their fate—a needle in the bottom—before he even comes through the door?

"Help yourself to the coloring book and crayons," the nurse said and gestured to the bottom shelf of the supply table. We helped ourselves and would have been happy to color in her books. In fact, we were poised and ready, but there wasn't an inch or a smidgen of clean space anywhere. The book was scribbled full!

"What *can* we color on?" I had asked. Two little-girl voices shouted the obvious answer to make me laugh: "The walls?" I was tempted! Then I spotted the big jar of tongue depressors, grabbed a handful, and for the next fifteen minutes we drew little people pictures on them, added cotton balls for hair, and lined them up on every available surface. We didn't have to wait for *him* again!

Perhaps I would entertain myself by taking his diplomas down from the walls and hanging them back, upside down. I'd done that once too.

Suddenly my mind snapped to the present as "Doctor Duck" marched through the door, his nurse right at his heels. We exchanged brief greetings and he introduced *"Maawgret"* (Margaret in any language other than southern aristocratic), whom I'd met on many other occasions. Still her presence always seemed to need explaining.

"*Maawgret* will be assisting me." I glanced her way, wondering if the two of them knew that I knew she was his star witness if a patient should decide to bring litigation against him for an impropriety.

"What seems to be the problem?" he asked.

I looked at him for a long moment, trying to summon my best business voice. I swallowed hard but the words came out in four awkward gulps: "Lump in my breast."

"Let's have a look," he said, gently opening my gown. I pointed to my left breast. For the next few minutes, I stared at his thinning scalp as he examined my breast thoroughly, grinding his fingers, it seemed, into every millimeter of flesh. The nurse, bent slightly at the waist, tilted her head this way and that as she followed the movements of his hands.

"Does this hurt?" he asked as his fingers dug deep into the soft tissue.

"Uncomfortable, yes. Hurt, no," I replied.

"How about this?"

I shook my head.

"And this?"

"No."

Next, he was squeezing my nipple. As he squeezed and released, squeezed and released, he fired rapid questions.

"Any discharge?"

"No."

"Bleeding?"

"No."

"Pain here?"

I shook my head.

"Here?" he asked as his hand moved off target center.

"No."

"Puckering? Change of contour?"

"None of the above."

With each question his nurse watched my eyes carefully. Almost before I'd formed my answer, her head would bob as if it were on a spring, as though she was trying to beat me to my answer. Maybe every other woman that day had said no to the questions and she expected the same from me. I suddenly felt I was on some sort of conveyor belt—that it didn't matter what I said because my diagnosis would automatically be identical to patients A, B, and C who preceded me.

I looked at the ducks while the doctor checked my right breast as thoroughly as he had the left. When he finished, he buried his head in my chart, and in his doctor-style mumble, reviewed my gynecological history without seeming to take a breath: Two children, seven years on the pill, two lumpectomies, IUD lodged in the wall of the uterus and suspected pregnancy, hysterectomy, hormone tablets. He glanced at me as though we shared a secret. "They did the trick, didn't they?" he asked. "The hormone pills."

"No more hot flashes. And my sex life improved . . . considerably!" I answered.

A few more mumbles, then he shut the folder and suggested I dress and join him in the next room. I knew his procedure well; the examining room was for examining, the office next door was for discussing his findings. He always used colorful illustrations with his explanations. I'd seen his pictures of healthy ovaries and diseased ovaries, healthy uteruses and diseased uteruses, likewise fallopian tubes and every other healthy and diseased gynecological probability. The businesswoman in me liked this *modus operandi*. It seemed much more humane and dignified to have a discussion fully clothed, sitting eye to eye across a desk than as some doctors did it, pontificating while you lay on your back on the examining table.

I stood and reached for my clothes. I pulled my bra out from under my folded blouse, under because that's where my mother had told me to put it. "It's not ladylike for your underwear to be in plain open sight," she had always said. I put on my bra and buttoned my blouse, comforting myself with the fact I'd seen no worry in the doctor's eyes. Neither had I felt any sense of urgency, which surely would have been present were my breast or life in danger.

Minutes later in his cluttered office, he reached for the ever-present medical illustrations. "This is a healthy breast," he said, pointing with his pencil. "And here we have a diseased breast." He carefully shuffled the pictures, allowing me to examine them closely. He then handed me a third illustration. "This shows fibrous cysts or tumors. They aren't malignant but they certainly are bothersome and can easily be misdiagnosed. Some studies indicate they're *pre*cancerous. That is, they could eventually turn into cancer."

The pictures looked alike to me. All three breasts were mottled, only the shadings seemed different, like the same photograph printed at different exposures. I waited impatiently. I wanted to scream, "Do I or don't I have a problem? Answer yes or no!"

"You just happen to have very lumpy breasts and we'll have to watch them. But I don't think you have a thing to worry about," he continued with a smile in his voice. "Just to be sure, though, I'll put you in touch with a breast cancer specialist." He jotted a name on a prescription pad and handed it to me as he pushed himself back from the desk.

I thanked him and stood to leave. Then I remembered one more thing. "I know I told you my breast didn't hurt when you examined it. It didn't, not then. However, it does hurt most all the time. I just can't pinpoint *where*."

"Well, that's probably a good sign," he said, ushering me out. "There's rarely, if ever, *any* pain with breast cancer."

It was several months before I looked at the name on the paper. During that time I tried to convince myself I simply had a good case of empathy with my mother. Even though we'd been a thousand miles apart, I'd had such sharp pain in my breast that it took my breath away at the very hour of her mastectomy two years before. It seemed logical I would be subject to other psychosomatic symptoms. Finally I made my appointment.

"Mrs. Buchanan, please take a seat and, if you will, fill out these forms for me," the receptionist said, handing me a clipboard and a pen. Filling out forms was near the top of my list of *un*favorite things to do. I could remember the name of every person I'd ever met, but could barely recall my own phone number and address, much less my parents' birthdays and the dates of our various illnesses and surgeries.

Scanning the small print, my eyes jumped to midway on the page. Like a neon sign in a window, the words flashed at me: *Cause of death? Cause of death? Cause of death?* I had to look up to clear my head. Finally, I managed to control my emotions and fill in the spaces: mother's maiden name, birth date, birthplace, if deceased give *cause of death*; father's name, birth date, birthplace, living, deceased, if deceased give *cause of death*. The words began flashing again.

Daddy had died of cancer at fifty-two. Mother had been diagnosed with breast cancer and had been given a less-than-hopeful prognosis. *Cause of death?* I tried not to think about it.

What I remember about this examination is the small towel. "Strip to the waist and lie down on the table," the nurse instructed as though she'd said it a thousand times before. "Lay the towel across your front," she added, handing me a small rectangle of terry cloth. When the door closed behind her, I did as I was told.

The towel was useless. If it covered one breast, it didn't begin to cover the other. I tried folding it into a triangle, thinking I'd use the old catty-cornered method. It still didn't reach. I tried lying on my side, resting on my elbow with my head propped against my hand. With the other arm, I held the towel in place. It felt like a pose for a sleazy magazine.

When the doctor appeared in the examining room half an hour later, I reminded him we'd been on an Easter Seals telethon together a few years earlier; he just looked at me as though he didn't have the vaguest idea what I was talking about. He was neither as suave nor as sophisticated as I'd remembered him. He was large, had a bush of unkempt hair, and looked middle-aged (*provided* his life expectancy was one hundred and thirty!).

"Does this hurt? How about this? And this?" he asked as he poked and probed my left breast. It didn't. Then he repeated the procedure on my right breast. When finished, he tried to cover my chest with the postage stamp towel. I gave him no assistance; it lay between both breasts, covering neither.

I watched as he matter-of-factly made notes on a little yellow scratch pad. "A mammogram ... you'd better have a mammogram as a precaution," he muttered as he wrote. "I don't *feel* anything or expect to find anything, but it never hurts to check it out." He glanced at me and then stepped toward the door.

"Just a minute," I said to his back. He stopped. "My breast does hurt. Well, not exactly hurt, but there is an aching—an overall discomfort—I can't explain."

He turned and smiled. "That's actually a pretty good sign that there's no serious problem. There's no pain with breast cancer." With that, he disappeared.

I can't recall anything about the mammogram or even where I went to have it. I only remember "too-small-towel" doctor calling a few days later and telling me everything was fine. Before hanging up, he, too, said not to worry.

Idiot! Of course I'll worry, I thought. *I'm out of my mind with worry.*

For the next year, I tried to force the thought of cancer from my mind, but the pain in my breast became more than a heaviness. It became very real. I sometimes awakened in the morning with my right hand cupping my left breast, knowing that I had been trying to comfort it even in my sleep.

I remember one such morning in particular. It was the day after I attended the funeral of my friend, Julia, who died of breast cancer. I lay there in bed unable to move because of the honest-to-goodness pain. It was quiet in the house. I turned over on my right side. The sensation was worse without the mattress beneath my breast. I lay on my back; the pain persisted. With a sigh, I rolled back to my left side. My mind began to play "What ifs?" *What if I have cancer? What if I die? What if I leave my children motherless? What if Wayne likes his second wife better than me?*

No pain with breast cancer. If I had a quarter for every time I heard that, from my various doctors and friends who quoted *their* doctors, to the interns who examined me in the hospital the night before my surgery, I'd have money for eye shadow for this life and the next. Mother's doctor had also insisted there is no pain with breast cancer; yet she suffered a gnawing, toothachey pain long before her malignancy was diagnosed.

My fear of cancer grew as the months passed; my mother's hold on life became increasingly tenuous. I'd seen my beautiful, life-loving mother grow weaker. Lose hope. Give up. I'd seen her body become emaciated—and, dear God—I was haunted by the vacant stare in her eyes. In those eyes, I began to see my own reflection and it scared me. *No matter what the doctor says . . .* I thought to myself. Though I still couldn't feel a lump, I decided it was time to go *doctor shopping*.

One day when I had a slight cold, I called a physician's listing service and was given the name and phone number of Edmond Tipton. I was told he had recently set up practice and was looking for patients. I made an appointment and decided to put him to the test. "I'm doctor shopping for myself and my family; here's what I want. I want you to know who we are when we call or visit. I want you to remember our names and something about us. Fake it if you must. I want you to take our phone calls or at least get back to us right away. And I don't want to wait unreasonable lengths of time to see you." I took in a quick breath, and continued, "In return, we'll pay our bills on time. We'll speak highly of you. And we won't call you unless absolutely necessary—that includes in the middle of the night. Take it or leave it!"

Grinning broadly, Dr. Tipton stuck out his hand and said, "It's a deal!" He was the only doctor who examined my breast who didn't tell me not to worry. He listened to my story, checked me thoroughly, and admitted he didn't have an answer. Then he said something very important, something I wish everyone could hear. "If you listen to your body, it will usually let you know when there's a problem," he said. "And I think we should keep looking until we get an answer. Let's get a specialist to examine you, a surgeon who sees a lot of these cases." I didn't ask what cases he was referring to, but the words and the fact that I was being referred to a surgeon made my stomach turn.

A few days later when I arrived for my appointment with the surgeon, I was tired of the forms, tired of answering the same questions, tired of the unknown, tired of taking off my bra and tucking it under my blouse. *This is it*, I thought. *There's not a thing wrong with me. There are women who go from one doctor to another looking for God-knows-what, and I don't intend to be one of them. When this doctor tells me I have nothing to worry about, I'll never think about it again.*

I sat on the examining table with my feet dangling off the end. Within minutes, the doctor scurried in, before I could even think about turning his pictures upside down.

"What seems to be the problem?" he asked without a hint of a smile. Why couldn't he at least say, "Hello, nice day." *I get a better welcome from the man at the cleaners and spend a fraction of the money*, I thought to myself. I bit my tongue.

As I regurgitated my recent medical history, this new doctor stood with his hands on his hips like a cowboy. He listened intently, one eyebrow cocked. I told him about the heaviness. The pain. The feeling of foreboding. I had no more to say; but for some reason he intimidated me with his fervent gaze, so I kept right on talking, babbling as if I were stupid.

"Well, you know, my mother has breast cancer. She's dying in fact, and my father died of cancer. Only fifty-two! And then just recently I went to a funeral in West Virginia for a childhood friend who had breast cancer. I know this other woman who has cancer, actually several women, and I'm sure it's just all in my head, probably psychosomatic, but then I guess it should be checked out . . ."

"I don't feel any irregularity," he said after I'd finally shut up and he'd examined my breasts, "but you have such large breasts it's hard to tell."

"Try one more thing," I suggested. "Let me show you where to put your hand." The humor didn't escape me. I thought it was probably the first time a naked-to-the-waist woman had to show a man where to put his hand. I sat up and placed his hand on the left underside of my breast. His hand dug into my flesh as he frowned at the ceiling.

"Well, here again, it's hard to tell. There may be a slight thickening there. How about pain? Is there pain?"

"Yes. Sometimes. Well, almost continually. No! All the time. Yes, all the time," I babbled self-consciously.

"Don't worry. There's no pain with breast cancer," he said rather gruffly. "Unless, of course, it's in the latter stages." My stomach did a flip at that. *Thanks for the comforting words!* I thought.

"I see a lot of women and I don't think you have cancer. Just to be sure, let's get a mammogram."

"I just had one a few months ago; it was clear."

"We'll have another and it'll be a good basis for comparison," he said. Then he turned on his heels and was gone.

As I headed for the parking lot and drove down West End Avenue to have a mammogram, my brain tried to sort out the mixed signals it was receiving: *Nothing to worry about*, on one hand; *Unless it's in the latter stages*, on the other.

Since my first mammogram, our company, Dynamic Media, had produced several videos for the health care industry.

I'd acted as director, so everything was familiar to me. We'd filmed the mammogram process more than once: the waiting room; the forms; the cold, sterile machines; the helpful technicians. I wished for my own cameras and crew, and I wished—oh, how I wished—for an actress to play my role. We'd finish up, then we'd all go have a cup of coffee. This wasn't a film. This was real life and the life on the line was mine.

I felt big and bulky next to the slim little technician and wondered why I was always so embarrassed for another woman to see my breasts. I figured she probably saw hundreds a week, but I couldn't help wondering if she went home at night and said to her husband, "I had a patient today with the biggest—or the smallest or the weirdest—breasts I've ever seen!" Probably not. Just routine, all in a day's work.

She touched my shoulder as she guided me toward the big cylinder of a machine and the horizontal, stainless steel surface that would support my breast. "Step as close as you can, open your gown, and place your left breast on the shelf," she said, gesturing as if acting out the procedure. When my breast was in place, she adjusted the shelf for my height and pulled another steel plank down, sandwiching my breast between.

"At least you give me something to work with," she laughed. "If you ever want to give some away, I could use it," she added, pointing to her own chest. "It's almost impossible to get my flat-as-two-fried-eggs into position for the procedure." We both laughed. She stepped behind the partition—her protection—and the machine whirred. Before disappearing with the film, she asked me not to dress until the radiologist was sure he had a good picture.

The wait seemed to take longer than it should have; when she finally returned, it was to report that we needed to repeat the process. "Sometimes we just get a bad shot," she said. She then took several more exposures.

Again I waited. *They don't know what they're doing*, I told myself, preferring to think they were incompetent rather than to admit something might be wrong with my breast. After what seemed like an eternity, the technician told me I could dress. I'd be called with the report.

The next day was a busy one, so I didn't think once about the mammogram. After all, it was nothing to worry about, just a safeguard, right? I had a client in my office, and we were excitedly reviewing his projects when my secretary buzzed the inner-office phone line. "I normally wouldn't interrupt," she apologized, "but it's your doctor; he says it's urgent."

I punched the flashing button.

He said his name and then: "I just talked to the radiologist on your mammogram and it looks like there's a problem."

My mind raced. "What do I need to do?" I asked, careful not to let my client sense my concern.

"Well, we need a biopsy. I wouldn't wait if I were you. When can we arrange it?"

"Tomorrow," I answered numbly and hung up. My client surely must have been puzzled. I hurried him through his appointment. Later I couldn't remember what we had discussed.

When I was finally alone in my office, I sat at my desk, mindlessly shuffling papers. The timing couldn't have been worse. Mother had been admitted to the hospital again; I planned to leave immediately for Florida to visit her. What excuse could I give her for not coming? I didn't want to alarm her, but how could I possibly keep my secret from this person with whom I had shared everything? She was the only one in my life who could hold me, rock me, and understand my fear that I too might be dying of cancer, but I knew that it wasn't possible.

I didn't know where I had heard it, but the aphorism: "Just when you figure out what life's all about, you die!" flashed into my mind, followed by, "The only sure thing in life is death." I'd heard a television preacher say that. And then I remembered how, years before, Aunt Annie would read the obituaries aloud and pronounce to all who would listen: "It'll getcha someday. Sure as shootin', it'll getcha!"

Scenes from the past reeled through my head like motion pictures. When I was little, my cousin Nancy died of spinal meningitis, and they put her in a glass-top casket just like Sleeping Beauty. Until then, I thought just old people died. As I grew, my perspective changed about who was old. Daddy was young when he died at fifty-two; it seemed so unfair that he would never know my children. I wished he could have lived as long as Grandma Nelson, who died at ninety-seven. She fought death tooth and nail, hanging on to her last breath as long as possible.

I had no doubt I would go to heaven and eternal life when I died. I had learned a Scripture verse when I was a child that said, " . . . to be absent from the body, . . . [is] to be present with the Lord" (2 Corinthians 5:8 KJV). I wasn't *afraid* to die, but at forty-five, I certainly wasn't *ready* to do it!

Then again, maybe I wouldn't be ready even when I was old. Aunt Lucy, who was old when she died, always said, "The longer you live, the longer you want to live!"

When any of my mother's relatives died, their bodies were brought to the "old home place" in southern Ohio. Located miles from town and the nearest hotel, the house was big enough to accommodate all who wanted to come for the wake, which usually lasted two or three days. Since someone died fairly often in our extended family, I got used to walking through the dimly lit parlor in the middle of the night, past the casket, to the bathroom. As children, my cousins, Nancy, Dianne, and Janice, and I sometimes tried to scare each other by saying we saw the dead person move or by telling horror stories about people waking up six feet underground and trying to claw their way out. I never believed any of that, though. I actually thought of death as a peaceful, natural thing, especially if the person was in heaven, as I'd been taught.

My mind drifted back to Daddy's final days. Even though he had a year of dreadful suffering, his last day on earth was a bright and shining moment in my memory. The sun streamed through the windows of the back bedroom where he lay wracked with pain and weighing less than sixty-five pounds. His last words to me were: "It's so beautiful!" His eyes were shut, and I knew he was seeing something I couldn't see.

I left his room (the one he shared with Mother to the end) and walked to the kitchen door. I gazed out over the backyard which was level for about twenty feet and then sharply angled into a steep hillside. Even though the sun had been blazing moments before, a light rain was now falling. As I stood in the doorway, I realized there was a beautiful, but mysterious, path of yellow rose petals stretching up the slope as far as I could see. I opened the screen door and stepped out onto the porch. The fragrance of roses was overwhelming, as was the peace that blanketed my spirit. Later that day, as I talked about my experience we found there were no yellow rosebushes in our yard or in the neighbors' yards. I read somewhere that "coincidence is God's way of remaining anonymous." The rose petals, perhaps, were put there by a loving heavenly Father—or one of His angels—who cared enough to send the very best.

After a few minutes, I returned to Daddy's room. The sun was once again streaming through the windows. His breathing had stopped. He was gone to investigate what he had glimpsed and pronounced "beautiful" only moments before. As I looked at his still body, a long-forgotten Scripture made its way through the foggy corridors of my mind: "Blessed are the dead who die in the Lord from now on. . . . they . . . rest . . ." (Revelation 14:13).

Sitting in my office, shuffling papers and thinking of these things, I felt comforted and peaceful. Death was not to be feared. But then, my mind began to fast-forward to the present. I began thinking about the reality of tomorrow's biopsy, the probability of the diagnosis, and the awful finality of going through the rest of my life without a breast—or worse. Wracked with all of my old fears, I buried my head in my hands; hot, vulnerable tears filled my eyes. Tomorrow was just a day away!

THREE

No Mastectomy?!

I woke early. As I lay in bed, my mind bounced around like one of those balls connected by a rubber band to a wooden paddle. "It's cancer, I know it's cancer, I'll be dead!" *BOING!* (The ball hit the paddle!) "I'll live, I'll live. The biopsy will be benign." *BOING!* (It hit again!) "I won't see my daughters grow to adulthood." *BOING!* "It's cancer, but I'll be brave, I'll be strong so strong people will think I'm a saint." *BOI-OI-OING!*

The paddle ball dialogue continued as I dressed and drove to the doctor's office—and didn't stop as I sat in the waiting room. After a few minutes I was called into the inner sanctum. The wait there was brief, perhaps because I was the first appointment of the day; or maybe, just maybe, he understood the agony I was going through. He spoke very positively.

"I'm just not convinced of a malignancy. It's certainly not clear from the mammogram," he said, as once again he examined the breast in question.

"Probably nothing; but if we do get in there and find a problem, we'll need to take the breast." *BOING!* I wanted to pound my head to stop the interference.

"Not at all like we used to do," he continued. " . . . used to do a radical, take *everything*." He began to explain what he meant by everything, but I didn't listen. I knew! With Mother they'd taken everything. Her poor chest looked as though she'd been attacked by a maniac with an ax. It was concave and discolored; even the movement of her arm was severely impaired. Yes, I knew!

"Today we do what's called a modified radical. It's much less disfiguring," he said as though he expected me to be overjoyed. He explained that along with my breast he would remove and test lymph nodes, and if there was *node involvement* (words I would hear often in the future), he would recommend an oncologist to oversee my chemotherapy—*BOING!*—or radiation—*BOING!*

The words were scary to me. Chemotherapy! Radiation! Mother had had both. I didn't want to think about it. After I dressed, he asked me to sign a form giving permission to do a mastectomy if a malignancy was discovered.

"If you were my wife, I'd want that cancer out of there in a hurry." His words made sense, and I signed without a second thought. He patted my shoulder. I left.

With nothing better to do, I drove to Rebecca's Lingerie Shop to buy a new nightie. Rebecca's is the place to go when you want something really special; I'd had enough *really specials* that Lillian, who waited on me, knew me by name.

"So, Suzanne"—the name on my checks—"what's the special occasion?" The ball hit the paddle!

Lillian listened as I explained, then she hugged me. "You're a beautiful woman," she said. "I hope you don't have to have a mastectomy; but if you do, you'll still be beautiful and Rebecca's carries prostheses and the necessary bras." She seemed pleased to be able to tell me that, as if to say, "one less thing to think about."

"Let's not even worry about that right now," she said.

My purchases included an elegant robe, matching gown, and a cute little short number that showed off my legs to their best advantage. I bought not one, not two, but three one-of-a-kind satin pillowcases with antique lace "out to there."

At around three in the afternoon, Wayne went with me to the hospital. Waiting for me in the admitting office was the most gigantic pot of yellow daffodils you can imagine—so beautiful and so obviously out of season that they were oohed and aahed over by each passerby. Somehow I knew before I looked at the card that they were from my friend Joy.

I filled out the forms, checked into the assigned room, donned my elegant peignoir, and stacked my satin pillows behind my back. Various busy little hospital bees buzzed in to draw blood, take temperature, measure blood pressure, spout questions, and check off lists. One of the practical nurses was a big, beautiful, black woman whom I loved immediately. She knew how to bypass the usual necessities of conversation and get to real talk.

"Oooh, girl . . . look at you! . . . all those fancy pillows. This looks like a house of ill repute!" She twisted the words around her tongue and spat them out like a mouthful of spoiled cottage cheese.

"What're you two gonna do in this room?" she chattered as she worked. "I better shut that door 'fore somebody looks in here."

Some folks came to recite their well-rehearsed speeches and move on:

- "Hi, I'm your anesthesiologist . . . just stopping by to intro-duce myself and tell you the procedure for tomorrow morning."
- "Excuse me. I'm your dietician with your menu for tomor-row; however, our IVs are actually tastier than our food."
- A battle-ax of a nurse marched through the door with nail polish remover and a ball of cotton. "Remove the polish from your fingernails and toenails. I'll be back to check." No excuse me, please, or thank you. I didn't argue with Big Nurse Battle-ax. I removed!

Late in the afternoon Joy came, and Wayne left me in her care to go to the office for a while. He promised to return later with something decent to eat.

"Joy," I said when we were alone, "I think I've made a mis-take. I shouldn't have signed that paper giving permission for them to do a mastectomy. First of all, I don't want to be put to sleep wondering whether or not I'll wake up without a breast;

secondly, I've read there is a possibility of error—though a remote one—and they could remove my breast unnecessarily."

"Well, go to the nurses' station and get your paperwork and we'll change the doctor's orders," Joy said with bravado. Joy and I had met twenty-five years before when our husbands were in business together. We became best friends practically at first sight, and through the years our relationship has only grown stronger. I call her my unofficial publicity person because often when I meet somebody new, they'll say, "Oh, so *you* are Sue Buchanan! I'm so glad to meet you! Joy MacKenzie has told me all about you. She thinks you are wonderful!" Then, of course, I have to try to be wonderful and live up to that person's expectations. Now that I think of it, it hasn't been easy being Joy's friend!

"Can I do that?" I asked. "Can I change the doctor's orders?"

"Hey, it's your body," she answered. "Of course you can. Probably make the doctor mad, but you can do anything you want to do. You're paying the bills."

"Probably make the doctor mad" was the understatement of the day. I *did* change the orders. Joy went with me to the nurses' station where I asked for my records and a pen.

"NO MASTECTOMY!!!" I wrote across the top of the page and again in the margin next to where I'd signed my permission— three exclamation marks and all. "LUMPECTOMY ONLY!!!"

Perhaps it was because the nurse had given me a wide-point magic marker, but I'll have to admit, the words did have an angry look about them. We went back to the room.

It wasn't five minutes before the surgeon, in his wrinkled scrubs, bolted through the door and assumed his cowboy pose— eyes a-flashin' like a coyote had got his best longhorn. He stared at me and my pillowcases for an inordinately long time before he spoke. In fact, it was body language he spoke and I'd never seen it spoken more fluently! He looked riotously funny in his green shirt, green pants, green hat, and green booties. He looked like a big, mad, green frog! After a few seconds Joy and I burst into laughter. He glared! The more we laughed, the more he glared and the more he glared, the harder we laughed.

Finally he spoke; although I've forgotten the exact words, he said basically that I was a stupid woman who couldn't face reality; and no matter what my reasons, I shouldn't question his superiority. I tried to explain that I fully intended to have the mastectomy once the reports were in; but before I could get the words out of my mouth, he told me in no uncertain terms that having two surgeries was ridiculous when it could all be taken care of in one. His glaring intensified!

As crazy as it may seem, Joy and I were struck with another round of laughter. Joy was literally bent double, holding her stomach, and tears were rolling down my cheeks. However, you sober up quickly when it occurs to you this isn't the way to treat a person who, in just a few hours, will be standing over you with a wide assortment of sharp knives.

Disgustedly he threw his hands in the air with a "Hurrumph!" and with an I-give-up-and-I-don't-like-it-one-bit gesture, he left the room. But not before Joy taunted, "Your clothes are wrinkled too." We both knew he heard and we knew it was rude, but once again the giggles hit, and we laughed until we couldn't laugh anymore. This was a turning point for me. Suddenly I was in control and I liked the feeling. I would be making the decisions for my own body from now on.

The evening was a pleasant one. Wayne was there along with my daughter Mindy, who was in high school. Mindy is one of those people who can walk into a room, move a few things around, and suddenly make a blah room look homey and comfortable. After she had worked her magic touch on the room, she kissed me, smoothed my hair, climbed into bed with me, and leaned back against the gaudy array of pillows.

"I'm staying!" she announced.

My older daughter, Dana, was in college in Indiana and would keep in touch by phone. Friends dropped by, and each person commented on fancy me in my fancy gown in my fancy bed. At nine, everyone left and I didn't feel so very fancy. I dreaded a sleepless night of unanswered questions. Just then there was a rap at the door and handsome male eyes peered around the corner.

"Your friend Carlana told me about you," he said as he came into the room and turned a chair in my direction. I figured from the clues—a dangling stethoscope and a scrub cap *gollywompased* over one eye—he was a doctor of some sort. When he said his name, I recognized it to be that of one of Nashville's finest plastic surgeons.

He sat down, his long legs stretching halfway across the room. I suspected he'd had a long day.

"Do you know about reconstructive surgery?" he asked.

I was embarrassed to admit that this was one more thing I knew nothing about. The verbiage of the last two days had proved me ignorant of so many things: *lumpectomy* vs. *mastectomy*, *node involvement*, *chemotherapy*, *radiation*, *prosthesis*, *special bras*. The list was endless. These were issues I never needed to know about before, and at the time they weren't turned-inside-out reported on in the media as they are now.

"No, I don't know a single thing about reconstructive surgery. I've never even heard of it. Tell me."

"Right now, we don't even know if you'll lose your breast," he said. "If you do, then we'll make you a new one."

"And how do you plan to accomplish that?" I asked. " . . . think you're God or something?"

He quickly and easily picked up on the banter, giving me the impression that yes, if necessary, he *did* intend to play God in that one area of my life.

"Mind if I take a look?" he said as he pulled aside my gown. "Maybe, in this case I can do a little better job than God," he teased, as he looked at my large beginning-to-sag breasts. His face and tone of voice became serious. "There are different procedures, depending on the circumstances." He stood up and motioned for me to do the same.

"Bend forward," he said and I did as I was told. As I bent he took a handful of my stomach, gave it a little shake and said, "Be glad for this." Then he explained he could rebuild my breast from my stomach fat. That was the craziest thing I'd ever heard. My mind immediately did a good-news/bad-news joke on me: *The bad news is you might lose your breast. The good news is, you're fat!*

"Let's get the biopsy over. If it's malignant, come see me at my office; I'll talk to you about your options and show you pictures of patients who've had reconstructive surgery. I'll try to give you all the information you'll need to make a wise decision." He wished me luck and said goodnight. The mild sedative I'd taken earlier had begun to relax me, and soon drowsiness was overtaken by a deep, deep sleep.

In another part of the hospital my brother and sister-in-law checked in to have their first baby. They'd waited a long time for this moment; not only the usual nine months, but before that, a lengthy time of doubt and testing, wondering whether or not they could conceive.

The next morning I was kept groggy until time to be wheeled to surgery. Wayne came early and my brother stopped by to give me a progress report from the maternity ward. He told me that Becky was tired after such a long labor, but that everything was okay. "I've eaten every bag of peanut M&Ms in the vending machine," he added.

Joy was there to keep Wayne company. If anyone could buoy his spirits, it was she.

A nurse came to give me another needleful of groggy. I had a hard time staying awake. I had no worries. Finally the gurney pushers came. I kissed my husband, gave my friend a hug, and was whisked away and put soundly to sleep.

I knew nothing, of course, about what happened next. I often wondered how soon Wayne knew the results and who told him the bad news. If it was the doctor, I wondered what he said. One day I asked my husband to fill in the gaps.

"Want to read my journal?" he asked.

"What journal?" Imagine my surprise when he pulled a big red notebook off the shelf. He thumbed the pages till he found the right place.

"Read!" he said.

From where I was sitting, I could see him coming down the long hall. There were two nurses with him, one on either side. He was dressed in operating room green, and his scrub cap was pushed back on his head. He still had on the cloth shoe coverings that caused him to sort of shuffle as he walked.

Jon, Sue's younger brother, was sitting across the bed opposite Joy and me. He was beaming from ear to ear. After all, that's what men are supposed to do when they've just been presented with a magnificent baby girl (the first one) less than an hour earlier. He had never known such unrestrained excitement and justifiable pride.

Joy leaned over to me and nodded toward the hallway as if to say: "That's him, isn't it?" She didn't ask the question out loud; she knew I'd already seen the surgeon coming. My eyes were glued to him, and my whole body was tense, even though I like to pride myself in always appearing to be totally in control.

He came in and stood beside Jon even though he didn't acknowledge Jon's or Joy's presence. He was obviously in a hurry and wasn't there to exchange pleasantries or small talk. He looked and spoke directly to me, using as few words as necessary to consummate his mission.

"We completed the procedure and the preliminary lab tests show that the tumor is malignant—about the size of a lead pencil eraser." He held his hand out, pointing with his thumb to the tip of his little finger.

"Quite small," he said. "The final lab work will be completed later today and I'll know more about the type of cancer it is after I review the results of the culture from pathology. I'll be by tomorrow to discuss the next steps. Your wife is doing quite nicely; she's in recovery and should be back to the room in a little while. Any questions?"

That was like asking a drowning man if he'd like someone to throw him a rope—of course he would, but with a mouth full of water, how can he answer? *My* mouth was totally dry, glued shut with emotion; my mind was blank; my body was limp, and I felt numb. All I could manage to do was shake my head from side to side. Anguish rushed in to consume the optimism and hope that had been there just seconds before.

Jon broke down, sobbing uncontrollably. He'd been from the height of ecstasy to the depth of despair in less than two minutes. In that same hospital, on the very same day, within the span of an hour, his wife had given birth to their first child—a little girl—and he got the news his sister had cancer.

I sat there too stunned, too overwhelmed with my own grief to move, much less help my best friend, my brother-in-law. Joy, who had come to comfort, simply tightened her lips, touched my arm, then looked tearfully away, fully realizing there were no words appropriate for the moment.

By the time I came back to the room from surgery, Wayne had managed to pull himself together. No matter what he felt inside, I saw a smiling face and heard encouraging words. Other than a bandage on my chest I looked and felt the same. When I asked the question, "Was it malignant?" My husband answered that it was and repeated the doctor's words as to the size of the tumor, emphasizing "small as a pencil eraser."

Human nature somehow allows us to adjust information to make it possible to digest. I adjusted the information emphasizing the word *small* as I repeated it in my head. With a big grin Wayne changed the subject.

"You have a new niece," he said, and for the time being we were able to turn our thoughts to that happy event. He told me her size and weight and reported that Becky was doing fine. We discussed possible names and I wondered if anyone had told Mother, or if she was too sick to understand she had a new grandchild.

Later that afternoon Jon and Becky came to my hospital room and placed a tiny pink bundle in my arms.

"Cara Jane Davis, meet your Aunt Sue," my brother said.

I've loved Cara ever since that moment. Thirteen months later her sister, Kirby, arrived. Conception was easier the second time around! Redheaded, giggly, energetic Kirby! Cara is a lady, with a face like porcelain, heavy eyebrows, and eyes so expressive they practically speak—a good thing, since it's almost impossible to get a word in edgewise with her sister around.

When Kirby was older she would take a running leap at me, kiss me hard on the mouth, and answer, "Fine" before I could say, "How are you?" Cara would watch with those beautiful brown eyes, wait till Kirby finished her song and dance, and then move close for a hug. Now they are bright, energetic teenagers whose experiences are as important to me as those of my own children.

That day in the hospital, holding that less-than-twenty-four-hour life in my arms gave me hope and purpose for living. *They need me*, I thought and remembered Mother saying my brother Joe was born when her mother died and my brother Jon was born when her father died. Then she commented that it was "just like the Bible says: 'The Lord giveth and the Lord taketh away.'"

The Lord is giving us Cara and taking away my mother, I thought. And since Mother wouldn't be around to love Jon and Becky's children, it was all the more important for me to be there.

The Wonders of Pink Play-Doh

A few years ago a powerful publisher was asked if she had ever turned down a book that made her want to bang her head against the wall just thinking about it. She answered that, in fact, she had turned down such a book. The title of it was *I'm OK, You're OK*, which was picked up by another publisher and became a runaway bestseller. When asked why she rejected the book, she answered, probably with a grimace: "Because I was OK!"

I understand that. Before I had cancer, I was okay and had been all my life! Why should anyone *not* be okay either in mind or body? I suppose, to some extent, I thought health was something I could control with my mind. My parents taught positive thinking right along with Christianity. Instead of "Cleanliness is next to godliness," at our house it was, "Positive thinking is next to godliness!" Like my own parents, I had easy answers for my children.

"Snap out of it!" I'd say. "Stop mullygrubbing!"

God certainly didn't want us to mullygrub. I could think of a dozen verses from the Bible that said "Don't mullygrub." Not in those exact words, of course, but the message was there, not only for living, but for dying as well. In Psalm 23, I knew God promised:

Even though I walk through the valley of the
  shadow of death,
I will fear no evil,

for you are with me;
your rod and your staff,
they comfort me.

Daddy was a person who trusted that concept completely. He never complained, even though he suffered great pain from the ravages of cancer almost every moment for over a year. Theoretically, at least, I knew that when God decided it was my turn to die—bite the bullet, meet my Maker, walk into the sunset, shake hands with Elvis—I could exit, drawing from the same source of comfort as my father.

Even though I knew I had a malignancy and would lose a breast, this ingrained bent toward positive thinking drove me like a Mack truck for the next two days. I didn't mullygrub once, and I was in a constant state of *snap-out-of-it-ness!*

The night I came home from the hospital after the biopsy, Wayne and I mapped out a plan. We outlined the next two days and listed every person we knew who could give us information:

See: Dr. Plastic: reconstructive body work!
Dr. "Cowboy": surgery and to recommend an oncologist
Oncologist: treatment
2nd oncologist: 2nd opinion
American Cancer Society: literature and information
Lillian: prosthesis and bras
Phone: Doctor (shirttail relative) in Denver
Doctor (friend of friend) in Tulsa
Various witch doctors who use unorthodox methods
All the people we know who recovered from cancer to ask
    them how they did it

The next morning I hit the road running. First to the plastic surgeon. Visiting his office was like visiting close friends. I'm not sure I understood what it was that first day, but eventually I figured it out. Plastic surgery is in most cases elective (not like having to have your gallbladder out). These people understand marketing and that good clients (patients) beget good clients.

As I walked through the door, my eyes took in the beautiful waiting room. The furniture was arranged in conversation-friendly groupings, unlike the predictable chair-chair-chair-table-chair-chair of most doctors' offices. Not a duck or six-month-old *Newsweek* in sight, but rather, various *objets d'art* and big collector books. The receptionist wasn't in a cage! She stood up and came toward me.

"We've been waiting for you. I'm Rosemary. Are you doing okay?" she said, and she offered to share her banana bread. "Our patients bring us goodies all the time. I'm getting fat; look at this." She patted her perfect hips. My eyes took in her perfect face.

Of course, I wondered if she had partaken of the glories of plastic surgery, and yes, dear friend, I looked closely at each woman who came into the waiting room, and yes, I played the same guessing game: "Wonder what she's having done . . ." and "Wonder what she's had done . . ." and on and on. I played it that day and every visit thereafter!

It seemed that everyone in the office was just waiting to meet me, to answer my questions, to help me in my crises. The first thing the doctor did was show me a scrapbook. The pictures there were unbelievable. On the first page there were three pictures, obviously all of the same person even though the face wasn't visible.

My eyes barely glanced at the middle-aged sagging breasts of the first picture. Instead they were drawn like a magnet to picture number two: a maimed torso, minus one breast. In its place was a vicious, ugly scar. The remaining breast stared at me like some eye, some cyclops freak of nature. I sucked in my breath, and my eyes were glued to the atrocity. The doctor didn't try to use words to soften the blow. He waited until my eyes moved on to the next photograph.

"What's this?" I asked in awe. "A reconstruction job?" He simply nodded his head in affirmation and I leaned close for a better look at this work of perfection. Two matching, pert, compact breasts, good enough for the cutest little cheerleader I'd ever met!

We continued through the book until I saw breasts very much like my own. I stopped and stared. Big, white, weighty breasts.

Obviously the before shots. In the next picture one of those breasts was missing. I couldn't look! I'd seen all I wanted to see of mutilated chests. The third was the after picture. Sure enough, better than they were to begin with. No bag, no sag!

"I understand now why you were so smug the other night. You do give God some competition, don't you?"

He gave me a knowing look and chuckled. I couldn't help remembering a joke I'd heard:

It seems there was a lawyer at the gate of heaven who saw a doctor make his way past everyone in line, nod to Saint Peter, and walk right in. The lawyer, wanting justice, complained to Saint Peter.

"Who does that doctor think he is, going to the front of the line and walking right in?"

"That's not a doctor," Saint Peter replied. "That's God. Sometimes He likes to play doctor."

As though we had all the time in the world, the doctor drew diagrams in the air as he explained my options and described the various procedures. It was even possible to use a flap from my back and twist it around to the front and insert an implant. He showed me different kinds of implants and discussed the pros and cons of each. I held one and played it from hand to hand like a slinky toy. I knew about implants; some of my best friends had them, not because of cancer, but for aesthetic reasons.

He explained, in greater detail than he had at the hospital, how he could use my own body tissue—stomach fat and muscle—to rebuild the breast. He'd already *approved* my tummy fat.

"If you do it that way, you get a tummy-tuck in the bargain," he reminded me. What woman in her right mind couldn't see the advantage in that?

That first night he visited me in the hospital, I had wondered about the nipple, whether it could somehow remain intact.

Now I thought, *Of course not. The nipple will be gone, but a reconstructed breast with no nipple is better than no breast at all!*

"Did I explain the nipple?" he asked, as if reading my mind. I shook my head.

"In some cases we graft it to another area of the body for the duration of treatment and reposition it at the time of reconstructive surgery. We don't do it, though, when cancer cells are present because of the possibility of spreading the cancer. In your case we'll just make you a new nipple."

"The god syndrome?" I questioned, trying to pretend I wasn't overwhelmed by this new piece of information. "How do you manage that? Pink Play-Doh?"

He laughed and explained that recreating the nipple was the simplest part of the job. He would remove a small portion of skin from the inside of the top of my leg and sew it to the proper place to make the areola. With a few extra stitches he would create a sack that simulates (in looks only) a nipple. He explained that the skin pigment from that part of the leg actually resembles the normal brownish-pink areola color.

"If you have good insurance, it'll most likely pay," he commented. "The only negative thing is that we'll have to wait until after chemotherapy."

Today, in most cases, the procedure is done immediately—sometimes in two steps—using an expander to stretch the skin and later replacing it with a permanent implant. He suggested that even though reconstructive surgery was off in the future, he would come to the hospital the morning of my mastectomy and draw lines on my body to show my surgeon where to cut. He explained that often surgeons didn't take his needs into consideration—didn't leave him enough skin to work with—and that if care wasn't taken the scar might be visible above the dress line. Since my cleavage was much like that of the Queen Mother, I'd never worn very low-necked dresses, but I decided to take his word for it.

"One last detail . . . ," he said as he closed my chart. "Let's get some pictures." We moved to another room, and his assistant helped him adjust the lighting. We chatted like old friends, and when I left, I had the feeling they hated to see me go.

My next stop was the surgeon's office, and I felt much less brave than I had in the hospital with Joy present. In fact, as I sat in the waiting room I found myself rehearsing what I'd say when I came face-to-face with this doctor we'd so blatantly poked fun at. Maybe I'd just throw my arm around his shoulder and say, "Shoot, doctor, I don't know what got into me. I guess you just bring out the worst in me." Or I could blame Joy: "*She* brings out the worst in me and I've told her good-bye, so long, you're a bad influence!" I would promise never to see her again. Maybe I'd mention I'd met Johnny Cash. I'd heard he was Johnny's doctor. Couldn't hurt!

Before I decided which tactic to use, the door opened and the nurse read from my chart: "Mrs. Buchanan!" I could tell from her voice that word had gotten around that I was a troublemaker. I knew about troublemakers and what people in the medical profession thought of them.

Our company had produced several medical videos having to do with risk-management, which taught doctors how to manage their practices so as to avoid malpractice lawsuits. One important point was to keep good records. In our research we uncovered the fact that sometimes a doctor will write a nasty little acronym on a patient's chart. We found such codes as RFM, which stands for *Ready for Morgue*, and HSLT, for *High Speed Lead Therapy*—or more specifically, *shoot the patient!* A pediatrician scribbled UKD, meaning *Ugly Kid Disease*, and another physician wrote in the space marked "prescribed therapy," *Hold pillow to face for four hours—repeat every fifteen minutes.*

Once we were shooting a video on location in a Houston hospital where I personally saw a doctor write, *Sweet Potato Poisoning*, on a black man's records.

I couldn't see what my chart said—HSLT most likely—but the doctor's body language flashed the word *condescending* in neon! He was just too, too nice as he checked the incision, repeated the information he'd given me at the hospital, and told me he had arranged for the mastectomy the next day.

"Smaller than a pencil eraser," still had a nice ring to it, even spoken in "condescending-ese!" He offered, condescendingly, the name of an oncologist in his same building and condescendingly asked if I'd like his "girl" to arrange an appointment. I answered that I would. With something resembling a flair, he took my hand and helped me down from the examination table. He was so nice I hated to leave!

I was told I could see the oncologist immediately. I took the elevator down two floors, turned the corner, and entered the first door on the left just as I'd been instructed. The office staff seemed cold as Popsicles in the Antarctic, but the doctor seemed like a nice guy and a good photographer. His studies in black and white were displayed on the walls: cows, barns, old bridges, and junk-yard scenes. Being a photographer myself, I could relate. The same things caught my eye when I went out for the day with my camera.

This doctor had the greatest, most-direct, look-you-in-the-eye handshake in the Western world and was receptive to my, "Hey, I'm a photographer too." At least I thought I saw a glimmer in his eye that said he'd remember me if, by some far-out chance, I needed his services. Maybe homemade cookies would warm up the office staff.

I handed him the file folder sent from the surgeon and he opened it. Lymph involvement seemed to be the key factor in determining whether I would need his services. He explained, as had the surgeon, that during surgery lymph nodes would be removed from under my arm and sent to the lab for testing. If there were no malignant nodes, there would be no chemother-apy. If there was node involvement, the intensity and length of the treatment would depend on how many nodes were positive.

"Three months, six months at the most," he said. I liked him and since I liked his photography as well, I decided against a sec-ond opinion.

I went to my office and tied up loose ends with my secretary, and on the way home, I stopped at the American Cancer Society to pick up some brochures and books. Then I went home to spend the evening educating myself and making phone calls. Wayne and I talked to a lot of friendly, helpful people that night, but it's a blur now. Nothing changed the fact that the next day I would check into the hospital again and have my breast cut off.

That night Wayne held me close for a long time, and then we made love slowly—deliberately at first—and then so passionately I forgot what lay ahead. I fell asleep wondering if the same intimacy could ever again be achieved. Someone sobbed silently in the night. It must have been me, aware but not fully awake.

The next morning, in a mad frenzy, I bathed, shaved my legs, removed my nail polish for the benefit of Nurse Battle-ax, plucked my eyebrows, did laundry, cleaned out the refrigerator, grocery shopped, and went to the beauty shop. Then I called my secretary and went over the list I'd made while I was under the dryer.

Next I headed to Rebecca's where Lillian showed me the various prostheses and bra selections; she suggested I come back after my scar healed, at which time she would work with me to find the best choices. While I was there, I bought three more gowns and two more fancy pillowcases. I didn't need more pillowcases, but when I commented on how much I liked the ones I'd bought, one thing led to another. Lillian mentioned they were made by a very old lady and—actually it came to us both at once—this could be my last chance to buy more!

Late afternoon I checked into the hospital for the second time in a week. Friends filled the room for the entire evening, laughing, joking, and telling *remember the time* stories. I'm sure the nursing staff, as well as nearby patients, were glad when visiting hours were over. After my friends were gone, Wayne, Mindy, and Dana, who had come home from college, stayed behind. There were tears in our eyes as we kissed goodnight.

A needleful of groggy in my hip made sleep come quickly. The next morning my plastic surgeon was my first visitor. With a thick, black marker he drew a football shape on my left breast with one end of the football pointed into my armpit, the other toward the opposite hip. The *football* was bottom heavy and encompassed the nipple. He made markings around the nipple.

By the time my family arrived the IVs—with groggy added—were in place. I didn't give a rat's ankle what they removed—my breast, my leg, or even my head. The gurney pushers had to pick me up like a rag doll and put me on the cart. Just before they wheeled me away, the phone rang.

"For you," Wayne said and put the phone to my ear.

I recognized the voice of our close friend Doug. Doug and Laura Lee, friends of long standing, had recently moved from Nashville to Ohio. Even though my response was feeble, I was glad to hear his voice.

"Can I pray for you?" he asked.

"Yeah, hurry, I gotta go," I muttered. I'll always remember that sweet prayer holding me up to the heavenly Father and reminding me, as I was on the verge of slipping out of conscious thought, that I was His child—I was in His hands. I was ready to be wheeled into the operating room.

The first thing I remember when I awoke from surgery was a hallucinogenic-shaped woman hovering over me, repeating, "Suzanne! Suzanne! Do you know where you are? Suzanne! Suzanne! Are you awake? Suzanne! Suzanne! Do you know where you are?"

I was confused. Mother always called me Suzanne when she was angry, but this gossamer lady didn't appear to be angry. Her only intent seemed to be to pull me out of the long, dark anesthetic tunnel that felt so safe into acknowledged pain and the harsh lights of the recovery room. "Suzanne! Suzanne! You're in recovery." She stuck a thermometer in my mouth.

The day was a blur, but by evening, except for the six-inch-thick bandage and the knot in my stomach, I felt better. At least the anesthetic was wearing off. Dana insisted on spending the night in the room, and every time I awakened, she was there, rubbing my arm, stroking my hair, asking how I felt.

Dana later told me she had been trying to make up for being *rotten* (her word) to me over the past couple of years. She said that during the long night she kept wondering if perhaps she had caused me so much grief in her teenage years that she had *given* me cancer.

By morning I'd regained the will to live! Dana helped me adjust the bed so I could look in the mirror. I expected to see

Dracula's mother; but to my surprise, my cheeks were pink and my eyes bright. I patted my hair in place with my one good arm, poked around in the drawer for my makeup, and dabbed it in the proper places. I felt good and looked good if you didn't take into account the thick bandage around my chest under the yucky hospital gown.

I never felt really bad again after that first day. A pain here and a pain there, but mostly I felt numb in the area where the breast had been removed. Women often ask me what to expect in the way of pain, both for a mastectomy and reconstructive surgery.

"Think of the surgery as being done on the *surface* of your body," I say, " . . . rather than in your guts." That simplification helped me play down the pain and think of it as "no big deal." What I wasn't prepared for was the emotional pain of losing a breast and the bad prognosis.

Each postsurgery report was worse than the last. At first, the surgeon told us there were nodes involved. Next he said "a number of nodes" were involved. Finally, he said that there were fourteen malignant nodes. The oncologist said six months of chemotherapy, then changed it to nine. Finally he said, "A year of aggressive chemotherapy." A day or so after my mastectomy, the nursing school director came to visit along with several young student nurses.

"Do you mind if the girls drop in to visit with you?" she asked. "In class they're learning how to relate to their patients and this would help them apply what they learn." Of course, I welcomed the chance to advance the cause of medicine in my own humble little way.

One of the student nurses gave me her undivided attention, practically never leaving my side. She fluffed my pillows, stooped to help me with my slippers, opened my mail, and hovered in the background when visitors were present. She even came by after work. I thought perhaps she was just curious about me—this patient with froufrou gowns and bed jackets, satin pillows with lace out to there, and friends who climbed right into bed with her.

One day it slipped out, and I think she had no idea of what she said. She told me she was observing me, a patient facing death!

At about the same time, Dana had returned to college and was sharing her feelings with a friend, a doctor's daughter. After Dana poured out her fears and dread to this girl, thinking that of all people she would understand, the girl looked at her and calmly said, "Your Mother's as good as dead. You may as well get used to it."

The outlook wasn't great, but then again, you *did* hear about people who beat the odds!

I'll be one of those people, I thought. *I'll do whatever it takes. I'll offer up my veins to those rubber-soled people in white! I'll swallow their pills! I'll drink toad spit if necessary! I may complain, but I'll do it!*

five

Chemotherapy and My Cat, Ya

WHEN I THINK ABOUT chemotherapy, I think of my cat, Ya, my friend and companion during those dreary months.

I have been owned by many cats in my lifetime, some whose names I've forgotten. Some I named childish names like Baddie and Goodie because they were bad and good; and in fact I *was* a child.

At a very young age, dressed as "Mrs. Vandertweezers," I strolled the block with my cat, Smokey the Pirate Don Derk of Don Day, both of us dressed to the nines. I wore high-heeled shoes with holes that let my toes poke out, Mother's old satin blouse that came to my ankles, a wide-brimmed felt hat with a veil to the chin, black gloves with rhinestone cuffs, and an animal around my neck that bit its own tail. For days at a time I wouldn't answer to Sue, only to Mrs. Vandertweezers. Mrs. Vandertweezers, elegant lady that she was, felt her wardrobe rivaled that of any Hollywood star or that of the Queen of England.

Her regal companion, Smokey the Pirate Don Derk of Don Day, rode on his back in the doll buggy dressed in a doll dress and bonnet as Mrs. V strolled past Mrs. Eubanks' house, past the Liebles', past the convent, and past the Catholic school to Sacred Heart Catholic Church (as far as she was allowed to go), and back again.

"Hello, dahling!" she said to everyone.

"Everyone" was mostly the sisters walking back and forth between church, school, and convent. Sometimes Mrs. Vandertweezers and Smokey the Pirate were invited into the convent for a visit and some ice cream. Once they actually made a little turn through the foyer of the church; but they left hurriedly when Father Cuthbert came toward them—his robes flying—with his eye on Smokey the Pirate Don Derk of Don Day.

Going to that magnificent church and having a string of those nice tiny black beads, doing the little curtsy, and being slightly mysterious was more than appealing to Mrs. Vandertweezers. She gave Catholicism strong consideration. Naturally, she couldn't possibly become a nun because then she couldn't be *Mrs.* Vandertweezers or enjoy her lavish wardrobe!

After Smokey there was Agamemnon, the smartest cat ever to own me. He got his name from *The Four Little Kittens*, a book I still have after all these years. The book begins: "Once upon a time, there were four little kittens. Their names were Buzz, Fuzz, Suzz and Agamemnon." It ends: " . . . when their mother tucked Agamemnon into bed, she remembered he was the youngest and had tried the hardest. So she gave him an extra kiss on the tip of his nose."

My mother never let me kiss Agamemnon or my other cats on the nose or anywhere else. She said I would get a horrible disease. Now that I have had a *horrible* disease, I kiss my cats and wonder what Mother would think if she knew.

Among other manifestations of intelligence, Agamemnon could turn the piano light on and off. He would use his claws to grip the pull-chain. On and off it would go—a wonderful distraction when I was supposed to be practicing.

I still have the newspaper clipping that tells of Agamemnon's disappearance and my letter to the Great Scott, our local radio personality, telling him my "best friend" was lost and would he please help find him. I didn't mention that my best friend was a cat until the very last line.

Great Scott read my letter over the air, and sure enough, a listener heard my plea and discovered the "guest" in his home was not just an ordinary stray. He should have known! Strays don't stretch out over half the length of the buffet without touching a single piece of crystal. Strays don't sit by the refrigerator, looking at it through half-closed eyes, then look at you in the same manner, back and forth until you say, "Okay, okay, I'll feed you!" And strays *do not* turn lights on and off! The man brought Agamemnon home, and he lived happily with us for many more years.

We think of our beloved cat Ya every year at Christmas when I pull the Christmas tree skirt out of the box and admire its beauty. It wasn't easy, gluing on all those pieces of felt and tiny little sequins—ladies dancing, calling birds, French hens. Right over there by the swans a-swimming is a faded brown spot. We look at it each year and say, "Oh, that's where Ya threw up, God rest his soul!" A tear comes to the eye.

We got Ya when the girls were little. He made the move with us to Nashville and grew old and bored (not bored because of Nashville . . . he just did!). His only claim to fame was that he was true to a comment of Theophile Gautier: "He loved books, and when he found one open on the table, he would lie down on it, turn over the edges of the leaves with his paw; and after a while, fall asleep, for all the world as if he had been reading a fashionable novel."

Each week, Wayne and I read the Sunday newspaper; as we finished with the various parts, we tossed them to the floor and waited. Sure enough Ya would walk around on each section, sometimes stopping on the funnies or the want ads to take a bath, then curl up on the *Sunday Showcase* for a long afternoon nap. Always the *Sunday Showcase!* That is until I was executive of the week in the *Business Perspective*. That day he skipped the funnies and the want ads, didn't even glance at sports, fashions, or showcase. He went straight to the *Business Perspective*, looked at my picture, read the article, then chose that exact place to take his nap. We even snapped pictures to prove it!

I hate to say this out loud, but Ya loved cancer and loved chemotherapy. He was happiest during my year of bad fortune, and he made my life more bearable.

Treatment began five days after my mastectomy while I was still in the hospital. I've come to believe that beginning so quickly was an incredibly wise decision on the part of my oncologist. "Begin now!" he said. "Remember those cells are reproducing themselves at a staggering rate. We need to catch them before they get a head start on us."

Often a cancer patient tells me her doctor has said there's no hurry to begin treatment. "Get through Christmas . . . or vacation . . . or what have you," he'll say. It seems to me that the longer you wait, the more time you have to dread it. For me, the sooner the better.

The program he set up for me was pretty standard at the time. It called for bombarding my body with chemicals for two weeks and then allowing it to revitalize for two weeks. The bad news was that the drugs destroyed not only the cancer cells but the healthy ones as well. The good news was that the noncancerous cells replenished themselves at a faster speed than the others.

To begin my program each month, I was given my initial dose of medicine. On one of my first visits to the oncologist, the scene was so gloomy I wanted to run away. There were three or four women in very bad wigs and one in a turban. A man nodded to me and spoke. I recognized him as one of Nashville's most powerful lawyers. He was gently helping his elderly father who was very sick. So much for powerful! Even the rich and influential could not bypass all this.

The patients appeared to have one thing in common; their complexions had a putrid greenish cast. How soon would *I* be wearing a wig because of hair loss? How soon would *I* become bald and green? The waiting time in the reception area seemed endless, yet the hands of my watch had barely moved.

My name was called; I moved to an inner room lined with schoolroom-style chairs—the kind with a paddlelike arm on one side. In this case, the extension wasn't a surface for writing notes and assignments, but support for my arm which would be elastic banded so its veins would pop, then swabbed with alcohol, needled, and Band-Aided. Sometimes patted!

I had no fear of needles, but I dreaded the process of locating a suitable vein since mine are exceptionally small. Slap the arm, try for the vein. Slap the arm, try for the vein. Sometimes the nurse never found the one she was looking for—on the inside of my arm at the elbow—and had to use the one on the back of my hand where it caused ugly bruising and was a constant reminder of the painful procedure.

I had a favorite nurse named Pat, who could find the vein on the first try. I prayed each time that she would be available. Nowadays, a shunt can be inserted into the patient's chest and left there throughout the months of treatment. It provides a direct route into the body for the administration of the drugs. It's removed once treatment is finished.

Once the needle was in my arm, various cylindrical vials could be attached without having to insert a new needle each time. First the nurse attached an empty vial to the shaft drawing blood which she immediately handed to a technician who tested it for the telltale signs of cancer. Next, one by one, slowly and meticulously, the two medications were administered.

Next I went into an examination room, pulled off my clothes from the waist up, put on the sleeveless paper top as instructed, and literally held my breath, waiting to know the outcome of the blood test. I rarely had to wait long. Before the doctor even shut the door behind him, he told me what I wanted to know: "The blood work looks fine!" I appreciated the fact he didn't make me wait. I wonder if I ever thanked him.

"Let's take a look," he'd say as he poked around checking my chest, neck, and abdomen for lumps or swelling that might indicate a problem. Next he looked in my mouth and down my throat checking for mouth sores. On the days when my blood count was low, sure enough, my mouth was full of sores. Those times he postponed the treatment. Besides conversation about my health, we chatted. I was traveling back and forth to New York City on business at the time. He had been raised and educated there and loved recommending restaurants and jazz clubs to me. I returned the favor by suggesting local restaurants to him. He'd been out of circulation, busy doing doctor things, and had no idea where to go in Nashville for a romantic evening. I introduced him and his fiancée to a quaint little restaurant in Clarksville an hour or so away. It was important to me to establish some sort of relationship with this person who was perhaps my link to life itself. I liked him and I knew he liked me.

As we talked, he wrote out my prescription for two weeks of pills, part of the total protocol, plus something for nausea. The nausea pills never worked. Thankfully, there are now drugs on the market that control nausea. A week later I returned for my second bombardment of the month, and except for the prescription, the process was repeated. Every other month I had a chest x-ray.

Because of everything I'd heard about chemotherapy, I had a mind-set against it from the beginning. I *expected* it to make me sick. The doctor's office smelled like a chemical factory, and the aftertaste in my mouth was how I imagined dry cleaning fluid would taste.

Right from the beginning, I fussed and stewed about this yucky stuff. In my mind, I called it every bad name I could think of. I regarded the visits to the doctor's office a nuisance. "A ridiculous waste" was my label for the time I had to reserve for recuperation after treatment. It was ridiculous that I had to put up with this interference in my busy schedule.

After a couple of months of fighting against everything chemotherapy represented, I forced myself to change my attitude. One day as I waited for the doctor to come through the door with his pronouncement, I couldn't sit still. I began to beat my fists against the padded examining table, mumbling the four-letter word I'd ascribed to chemotherapy. "--,--,--, it's nothing but--!" I said. The word describes it well, I thought to myself.

"I've really worked myself into a sweat!" I thought, and then it came to me! I shouldn't be fighting this. This is good. This could be my cure. *I must accept this medicine into my body, be thankful for it, trust it to work for me and make me well.*

From that day forward, I didn't mullygrub about chemotherapy. I waltzed into that little room, pulled off my clothes, put on the sticky little bolero, raised my hands to God, and thanked Him for it. "Dear God, take the medicine and put it where it will do the most good," I'd say as I ran my hands over my body; " . . . and thank You, God. Thank You from the bottom of my heart!"

Later, at home, I began to spend more time thanking God, not only for the medicine and the medical professionals, but for my husband who enjoyed making my life easy, my daughters who loved me dearly, and my friends who supported me in every way. One of those friends gave me a colorful book called *The Human Body*—a children's book; I began incorporating the illustrations into my prayers.

"This is a picture of a healthy brain, Lord. Help mine to be healthy and free from cancer." I did the same with the pictures of liver, lungs, and bones, the likely places breast cancer would metastasize. The pictures certainly didn't help God. He knew what my guts looked like. They helped *me*.

For the first two or three months chemotherapy only made me tired. I went home and slept the afternoon away after treatment, but each month I felt progressively worse, eventually throwing up at the thought of it.

Each time I went for chemo, Wayne took me and picked me up. He offered to go in with me, but I knew he needed to be at the office; I also knew sometimes a doctor tends to "talk around" a patient when a spouse is present. Instead, I wanted a strong partnership between my doctor and me.

My appointment was at one o'clock in the afternoon, allowing me a productive morning in the office. Afterward Wayne took me home and turned me over to Ya for the afternoon. Ya would curl into the curve of my body and we would both sleep the afternoon away. The nausea became progressively worse each month. It hit late in the afternoon and I was sick—so sick—through the evening and into the night. Ya was tolerant. When I was in the bathroom, he took the opportunity to have his evening meal and his bath; but each time I returned to bed, he was waiting to cuddle and comfort.

On the day of my treatment, I must have looked and felt worse than my childhood cat Agamemnon did after he'd been out for two or three days and nights at a time, doing whatever it is tomcats do! He used to drag his big, old, yellow body through the door, turn his ears back at the food we offered, flop down, and with all the energy he could muster, lick his wounds—sometimes bloody, once with part of an ear missing—and give us a look that said, "Do not disturb!" Then he'd sleep the day away.

On the day after my treatment, I'd drag myself out of bed, turn my nose up at food (the people version of cats turning their ears back), and lick my wounds. The nausea came now and then but lessened as the day progressed. Eventually, I'd try a piece of toast with a tiny bit of peanut butter. Dear friends, Ronn and Donna sent a fruit or juice basket each time I had a treatment, and I came to look forward to the goodies tucked inside. By evening I'd comb my hair, put on lipstick, and welcome my husband. By the third day I was back at work behaving like a normal person.

One of the worst things a chemotherapy patient has to deal with is loss of hair. I hated sitting in the doctor's waiting room with other cancer patients who were in that predicament. Women wore their turbans and wigs. Men sometimes wore ball caps; but more likely than not, they wore nothing on their heads at all, their bald heads shining like chrome on a Cadillac.

Nowadays, some women capitalize on their baldness. They jazz up their makeup (several cosmetic companies now train their artists to work with cancer patients), add dramatic earrings, and forget the wigs.

I was told my hair might fall out around the seventh week. Knowing that it would happen was bad enough. Knowing *when* it would happen gave me a permanent knot in the pit of my stomach. It occurred to me that being prepared might help. I would buy my wig ahead of time. Once I discovered that my insurance would pay for it, I decided to have one handmade, not only to match the *color* of my hair, but the style as well. Someone recommended a beautician who was a wig specialist and former cancer patient herself.

My new wig was a perfect match, but it didn't ease the knot in my stomach. I was told that someday I'd wake up and my hair would be on my pillow . . . or in the bottom of the shampoo bowl.

I wished it would happen and be over with.

One Saturday morning I hopped into my car and drove the three minutes it takes to get to the beauty shop. Hazel, the owner, greeted me with one of her usual comments about my hair's disheveled condition! "Did you come in an ambulance?" or "Were you hit by a truck?" or perhaps, "Too bad we don't have a back door!" I can dish it right back: "People ask me every day where I get my hair done." I pause to make her think it's a compliment. "They want to make sure they don't come here by accident."

Unlike the newfangled shops where boys and girls prance around in tight stretch pants, swing shirts, and hair moussed up to heaven, Brookmeade Beauty Shop is just an ordinary place for neighborhood women to get the same old hairdo week after week and pay less than fifteen dollars. There's not even an *e* on the end of shop, much less a shampoo girl; and there are no fancy name pronunciations for Hazel, Pat, Brenda, or Ann.

My daughter goes to one of those places that has an awning out to there with a la-de-da name on it: *Le Bon Ton*; *Rumours*; or *Monsieur Ricque*—whose real name is probably Ricky. "Thees ees not hair . . . I make eet hair!" says Gar-doun (perhaps Gordon?). "Ze freenge (fringe? bangs?) needs a treem (trim?)."

One day Dana's curiosity got the better of her. "Gar-doun, where were you born? Where do you come from?" she inquired.

"Tullahoma," he answered in the same manner he might have said "Pah-reee!" Tullahoma is a small town a hundred miles from Nashville.

The truth of the matter is, even if I were bald as a billiard ball, I'd still go to Brookmeade just to visit my friends there. After almost thirty years of sharing the ups and downs of life, these women truly are my friends.

You find out stuff in a beauty shop. Like the best diet—no one there has lost weight on it and no one ever will, but it's the best! Recipes are handed out as freely as advice for a failing marriage or who to vote for in the next election. If I were a politician I'd sit around a beauty shop for a few days and save money on a political analyst.

It's free therapy! Both physical and mental. In some ways a good hairdresser is more important than a good doctor . . . or lawyer . . . or psychologist! Most customers are soft-faced grand-motherly types who giggle and tease, and some have suffered almost as much as their favorite soap opera star.

I've seen neurotics, alcoholics, and women so wracked with disease that they must be wheelchaired in and lifted to the sham-poo bowl. When they leave, they have a new lease on life, not just because of a fresh hairdo, but because someone catered to their needs, listened to their complaints, and massaged their scalps. It occurs to me, that for some, it's the only time they are touched.

I don't want to paint Brookmeade Beauty Shop as a mini-utopia because it's not. This next bit of information is touchy. Certain dryers belong to certain ladies. Mrs. Bridwell's is the one in the corner on the left. It's not written down anywhere, it's just something we know.

If you don't want one of those gentle women to turn on you, don't take her dryer! There are frequent discussions as to which *is* and which *is not* the best dryer and sometimes the discussions are as heated as the dryers themselves.

It's not always verbal in a beauty shop. You have to understand the body language too. On some days you note a rigid determi-nation and an irrefutable look in the eye of certain patrons that says, "Don't slow me down." If eighty-four-year-old Eloise Mader, former principal of Gower School, is dressed to the hilt, it's because she has a plane to catch. Probably a Civitan trip.

When Mrs. Bridwell shows up in a silk blouse and her good pumps and Jessie shows up in a skirt and stockings rather than sweats and tennis shoes, it's a good indication it's bridge day and they intend to be there when the cards are dealt.

When Ann Poteet has her Bible and books spread out, she's on her way to teach her Bible class. *Don't make these ladies late!*

That eventful Saturday morning, Hazel and I exchanged our sarcastic greetings, and I waited for my turn, pulling the pins from my updo as we chatted. I noticed an unusual amount of hair attached to the pins as I laid them on the counter.

Don't think about it, I said to myself. Pat, my hairdresser, finished with her customer, motioned me to the chair, and as usual, began brushing the hair spray from my hair. I could see that something was wrong from her reflection in the mirror; it only took a moment to figure out what it was. My hair was coming out in handfuls!

"Let's go ahead and wash it—try not to handle it too much," she suggested. With one hand she whirled my chair around so fast she practically gave me whiplash, and with the other she raised the lid on the shampoo bowl, banging it hard against the mirror. Her quick, jerky movements made me know she was upset. Her tears made me understand how much she cared.

I shut my eyes and avoided looking into the honesty of her face while she shampooed, rinsed, and as usual, wrapped my head in a towel. Surprisingly, my hair was still there. It wasn't until she began to comb through it that we realized that most of my hair had disattached itself from my scalp and was matted—as though with chewing gum—to what was left.

It took two hours to comb through my hair. That day no one argued over dryers, bridge games were forgotten, and hairdressers and customers alike took turns combing and dropping the dregs into a brown paper bag. Everyone was crying—that is except for Hazel. Her way of handling life's crises is with sarcasm and humor; since neither was appropriate, she left—simply got in her car and drove away. Later, she commented, "How can I razz you when your hair is falling out?"

After that day in the beauty shop, not much more came out. I felt I was green, peaked, and bloated, and often so sick I could barely hold my head up. More and more I thought about the possibility of dying.

One night I awakened with a start and sat straight up in bed. A feeling of terror gripped me. It was as though I was being stalked. My body, and even what was left of my hair, was drenched in sweat. *What is wrong? Why am I frightened?* My mind played out all the possibilities. *Will I go through the discomforts of chemotherapy only to find out it hasn't done its job? Will I die? Might*

I be bedridden and a burden to my family? Will I see Dana graduate from college—Mindy, from high school? Will I be around for their weddings? Will I know my grandchildren?

The night terrors began to happen regularly, sometimes more than once a night. Often I would fall asleep at my normal time and awaken less than an hour later to spend the rest of the night in panic.

Then another problem arose. Each time I would awaken, my head would feel as though it were full of swarming bees. This only created more anxiety. *I'm going to die soon! The cancer has gone to my brain . . . dear God, I'd rather die right now than face this fear!*

When I mentioned my problems to my doctor, he pronounced them normal. "It's normal to have problems sleeping," he explained, "and the swarming in your head is called *fromication.*" I was happy to know it had a name! "It's a result of the strong medication." This he said while writing a prescription for more medicine! *A mild relaxer*, he called it. For a few nights it worked and I slept like a baby, but soon the problem returned. With the doctor's permission, I increased the dosage and again it helped. The next time, I increased the dosage on my own.

By summer, I was beside myself. *I have to find an answer, I'm going crazy*, I thought. *Perhaps I can get myself together while I'm in California.* (Our company coordinates much of the production for the Christian Booksellers Convention, which was in Anaheim that year.) *Hopefully working those fifteen-hour days will make me so tired I'll sleep when night comes.*

One day during the convention my friend Donna Fisher asked if I could find time to meet with June Wark, a mutual acquaintance. June had been my Avon lady years before when we lived in the same Chicago suburb. I'd bought practically all her products, hoping they would make me as beautiful as she was. I'd lost track of her—she now lived in California—and I was delighted to hear from her again.

We met in a lounge near the exhibit floor; and unlike the old June, who could lay the lipstick on the line, she was beating around the bush left and right. "I don't know if I should bother you with this . . . I'm slightly embarrassed . . . obviously I wanted to see you . . . but besides that . . . I think I'm supposed to tell you something." She certainly had my curiosity piqued, to say the least. *Spit it out, June,* I thought to myself.

"I think God is nudging me to say this . . . but . . . well, let me tell you my story. Twenty years ago I had cancer and God healed me . . . but that's not the issue. It was the fear I couldn't deal with! I would wake up in the night in complete terror. I didn't want to *live* it was so bad. A friend of mine came to me and said, *'June, I'm going to pray for you. I'm going to ask God to take away your fear. I won't stop praying till He answers.'* Sue, I can tell you the minute and the hour my fear went away! In fact, I was running the vacuum cleaner. I just felt free and I knew it was gone!" She paused and leaned forward and touched me, "Sue, am I supposed to be that person in your life? The person who prays till the fear stops?" She paused and smiled her winning Avon smile. "I think I am!"

When I arrived back in Nashville there was a gift waiting for me, from my friend Kate Rupert. When I unwrapped it I discovered a beautifully framed poem that still hangs on my bedroom wall:

Footprints

There was a man who died, and he reviewed the footsteps he had taken in his life.

He looked down and noticed that all over the mountains and difficult places that he had traveled there was one set of footprints; but over the plains and down the hills, there were two sets of footprints, as if someone had walked by his side.

He turned to Christ and said, "There is something I don't understand. Why is it that down the hills and over the smooth and easy places You have walked by my side; but, here over the rough and difficult places I have walked alone, for I see in those areas there is just one set of footprints."

Christ turned to the man and said, "It is that while your life was easy I walked along your side; but here, where the walking was hard and the paths were difficult, was the time you needed ME most, and that is why I carried you."

—Author unknown

The words were a confirmation of June's message—that I couldn't manage alone; that I needed God's divine help to take the next step and let go of the pills. When I did, I slept like a baby, and the terrors never returned.

My yellow cat stuck with me through it all. For a while after my treatment was over, he would meet us at the door, lead us to the bedroom, leap on the bed, and look at us expectantly. He seemed to be saying, *Come on, let's be sick some more!*

One day Ya didn't come when we called. We searched the woods—he never went far. Every day after that, we hoped as we came up the drive. Finally I knew he was gone forever, and I wrote *Eulogy to Ya*. A eulogy to a cat, you say? Yes, a eulogy to a cat!

Dear Ya,

I guess you're really gone. This morning a fluff of your yellow-orange fur skitted across the driveway; but when I reached for it, a gust of wind swept it up to the sky.

That's when I knew you wouldn't be coming back. I miss you and hope your last moments were peaceful. I would have liked to comfort you as you comforted me so many times.

I remember the day we got you. You were just a ball of yellow fluff in Uncle Jon's hand. Dana and Mindy named you Yata which is the Greek word for cat, because Grandma had been to Greece and learned that word. She told us how she laughed when she heard the Greek ladies call, "Yata, yata," and saw their cats come running. We thought it was funny too.

You grew big and beautiful; and although you "frowned" a lot, we knew you loved your family and enjoyed the woods on "your" property. We even caught you smelling the flowers on occasion.

There's probably not a cat heaven; but if there is, I suppose you've met up with Goodie (Baddie is probably in that other place), Smokey the Pirate Don Derk of Don Day, and my beloved Agamemnon. Perhaps you're all comparing notes on little girls you've known.

Statistics? I'm the Only Me!

"ALL WOMEN SHOULD BE Mexican and illiterate." A doctor said that to me not long after my mastectomy. We were discussing whether or not a woman should know the statistics of her prognosis. I was appalled! My daughters accuse me of being confrontive in such a situation: "When Mother takes issue with someone, she gets right in their face and sticks her finger up their nose!" An exaggeration, of course! However, had this not been a phone conversation, I might have been tempted to do just that. I merely shouted, "You can't mean that!"

His remark seemed sexist and very much like a racial slur, but I did my best to take his frame of reference into account. He lived and worked in New Mexico and he treated many Mexican women who were illiterate and unable to pay. I knew he was compassionate, caring, and tops in oncology. I listened.

"People don't need to know their chances. Most patients hear the negative when it comes to ratios. I may be wrong, but I think people sometimes die because they hear the wrong number. I just wish they were too ignorant to ask." I could hear the anguish in his voice.

His way of counteracting the negative statistics was ignorance. My friend Trish, who owns a cosmetic company called Aloette, believes it's a life attitude. I tend to agree. Sales in Trish's company are accomplished through home party demonstrations, and once a year the women get together for a sales meeting. They see new products, learn sales tips, and share success stories. The conference was in Nashville not long ago; Trish invited me to come to the hotel for the final meeting.

Wow! Such energy! Such enthusiasm! Three hundred women excited about beauty products. They cheered, they clapped, they jumped—some even stood on their chairs and jumped—and they cried. If their children acted like that, these women undoubtedly would be screaming, "Settle down this minute, or you can go to your room!"

The program was packed with opportunities for the women to exhibit their ardent zeal. As the meeting progressed with awards and recognitions, the crowd energy accelerated to what I thought was its peak. I hadn't seen anything, though, until they introduced Trish.

"And now, ladies, what you've all been waiting for, our founder, our leader, our motivator, Trr-iiiish!" She entered the rear of the auditorium and made a grand entrance down the center aisle, waving to the crowd, stopping now and then to touch the hands that reached for her—the spotlight catching the sequins on her dress, like the Christmas tree in Rockefeller Center. I sat spellbound as Trish spoke.

"Have you looked into the sky and seen birds flying in formation?" Trish asked. The ladies nodded.

"Have you noticed they fly in that V formation?" She swept across the stage making a V high in the air with two fingers. They nodded enthusiastically.

"Have you noticed that one side of the V is longer?" This time they moved forward on their chairs—their whole bodies nodded.

Her voice softened to a whisper. "Do you want to know why one side is longer?" Oh, they did, THEY DID; they'd seemingly lived for this moment.

"Because one side has more birds!"

There was a rush of laughter but it was cut short as she continued to speak. They didn't want to miss a word.

"I'm a very basic person and what I have to tell you is very basic. I'm going to tell you how you can be rich!" A cacophony of cheers!

Her showmanship down pat, Trish paused. Then in a you'll-never-believe-this tone of voice, she began her story. "Less than fifteen years ago, *I* [she laid her diamond-laden hand on her glittering bosom] was giving the cosmetic parties. My husband and I had just bought a new home without selling the old one; and the expenses of two houses were mounting by the moment. My parents loaned us $10,000, but that only increased the burden." Trish walked the stage with her head bowed. Her audience was with her.

"Then the unexpected." She paused dramatically. "I had to have emergency surgery!" The audience felt the knife. You could see it in each face.

"On top of all that [the audience was holding its breath, waiting to know what could be worse] as I leave the hospital, the doctor tells me I can't drive a car for a month." They sighed in unison.

"Well, ladies, how can I have makeup parties when I can't drive? And how can we make it through this financial crisis when I can't have those parties?" I could almost hear those women ponder.

Trish bowed her head again, then lifted it, smiling. "Ladies, the doctor said I couldn't *drive*, he didn't say I couldn't *give parties!* I simply found someone else to do the driving . . ." I turned to look at the nonplused faces that said, *Why didn't I think of that?*

" . . . and do you know what? I had the biggest month in sales I ever had!" She quoted a figure. "The very biggest!" In one great swell the audience rose to its feet. Cheering! Clapping!

Once again Trish moved in close to the microphone for the zinger.

"Ladies, what do you hear?"

With that introduction, Trish set the stage to address the plague of her company and every other company—negative thinking. And it's what every cancer patient—or heart patient or accident victim or substance abuse overcomer—must surmount.

"Women should be Mexican and illiterate" was the doctor's way of counteracting negative thinking. "What they don't know won't hurt them." I prefer Trish's way. It's an attitude adjustment.

Another story, courtesy of Trish, brings the subject down to the nitty-gritty. It seems a seventy-year-old woman in New York, named Josie Green, was dying of cancer. One day she managed to get out of bed and walk to the corner. She passed a neighbor who said, "Josie, you look good today."

She thought, *Well, maybe since I don't look so bad, I'll fix myself up a bit and go to the theater tonight.* So she went to the theater.

Afterward someone walked up to her and said, "Josie, you look ten years younger." The next day Josie said to herself, *If I look ten years younger, I'll just dye my hair and get around more.*

The next time she went out someone said to her, "Josie, you don't look a day over forty."

Well, if I look that good, she thought, *I'll move to California!* She moved to California, met a twenty-five-year-old man, and married him.

The next day she was hit by a car and died. Was Josie ever mad! The angels had to drag her across the floor of heaven to the throne, where she proceeded to give God "what for!"

When God could finally get a word in edgewise, He said, "Josie, I'm sorry! I made a mistake. I didn't mean for you to die! You looked so good I didn't recognize you!"

God doesn't make mistakes, of course; neither does He lose track of His charges. But I can just picture old Josie out there in California in her tight leather miniskirt and hot pink halter. She heard the right things, all right.

I wish everyone I talk to could hear the good stuff instead of bad statistics. One woman asked her doctor what her chances for survival were. When he told her they were 70 percent for a ten-year survival—based on the number of malignant lymph nodes—she was confident she would survive.

Yet the next day she told me she was going to die. "I have a gut feeling I'm not going to live," she said. When I asked her why she had gone from hope*ful* to hope*less* in a twenty-four-hour period, she told me she'd read different statistics from her doctor's, called him, and insisted he tell her the truth. He admitted her case fell on the line between two sets of numbers, but he had chosen to give her the more hopeful answer. It seemed she was more comfortable with the negative outlook than the positive.

I read about a man named Irving who was a statistician. He developed cancer and his oncologist told him his chances which were not good. From then on, he refused to fight for his life.

He said, "I've spent my life making predictions based on statistics. Statistics show I'm supposed to die. If I don't die, my whole life doesn't make sense." The story goes that he went home and died.

I was determined to be different. Unlike Irving, I believed in a God who performs miracles.

Not long after I began treatment, I saw an article in the paper that said studies had been done proving that state of mind has nothing to do with the prognosis and survival rate of a cancer patient. I didn't believe it then . . . and I don't believe it now. And what do you know, recently there have been articles *that agree with me*; a good healthy outlook does give you a better chance of surviving longer!

Once I heard my chances, I decided to disregard them. In many ways, I fell perfectly into the tabulations. *Let's see; she's forty-five, white, female, 5'8" tall, weight*—BLEEP. *Hmmm, let's throw in some medical stuff . . . metastatic adenocarcinoma present in fourteen of twenty-six ancillary lymph nodes. Well, looks like this one won't be around too long!*

I'm convinced the computer can't capture my exacts. I am the only, *the very only*, Suzanne Davis Buchanan, and I come from a long line of sturdy progenitors. Those Entsmingers, McKnights, Nelsons, and Braleys lived long, healthy lives. There are a million, maybe a trillion, other minuscule things that the calculations can never take into account—what I eat and drink, how much I sleep and exercise, or how often I laugh or make love. Neither can it know that I am wrapped in the loving care of Wayne, Dana and Barry, and Melinda, and I'm prayed for regularly by my brothers and their families, and a host of friends, including my Sunday night group—all of whom believe in miracles!

Furthermore, I doubt there will ever be a computer program that can look into the future to see whether a person takes the prescribed medication or flushes it.

Some Words Should Be Whispered

"My name is edna puckett. You don't know me. I'm just one of the little people." She pouts. Then she leans toward someone in the front row and in her most abrasive old-lady voice asks, "You can't see my underwear, can you?" The word *underwear* is spoken in a loud whisper and her eyes dart as though someone might come out of the woodwork to arrest her for saying it. Aunt Edna has opinions about anything and everything.

"Don't get me started," she challenges; but it's too late! She's off and running, waxing eloquent about whatever comes to her mind: those know-it-alls with tongue depressors in their pockets and stethoscopes dangling around their necks or those *deee*-mon rock-and-rollers who travel in buses with darkened windows.

Every family has a "character" person—mine was Aunt Annie; Wayne's, Aunt Naomi. These individuals are the perpetuators of the family name and the preservers and translators of family history. Though they usually lack training, they are at once psychologist, physician, parent, pastor, and philosopher. They freely dispense unsolicited advice in large doses, accompanied by the vigorous shaking of an index finger.

Aunt Edna isn't a real character anymore than Mrs. Vandertweezers. My friend Joy created her for a church skit and insisted I was the one to play the part.

Aunt Edna didn't go away after the play. Every so often someone calls to ask if she's available for a birthday party, and I pull her out of the bag—knotty little gray wig, sensible old-lady shoes, knee-high stockings, navy polyester skirt, red blouse, and ratty white sweater with a pin that says, *Over the hill, not under it!* Her rouge is uneven and her lipstick is smeared almost to her nose.

Her spiritual "gift," she says, is the gift of criticism. She's quick to tell the minister, whom she calls "preacher," she likes the *beginning* of his sermon and she likes the end to his sermon. Then, with a laugh, she suggests, "How 'bout getting the two closer together!" She also wants to know all the church gossip so she can "pray more intelligently."

Edna gets a little more wound up at a party than she does in the church's fellowship hall. She confides: "When I was young, I was a hot little number ... I once set a young man's tie on fire!" or "In my day, I was kissed more times than the pope's ring."

Aunt Edna believes words such as *cancer, underwear, backslide,* and *sex* should be spoken in a whisper. Her generation wouldn't think of saying such words aloud!

My generation wasn't quite so conservative. As teenagers we spoke the word *sex* aloud and were curious about it; but most of us, however, wouldn't have risked sex outside of marriage, mainly for fear of pregnancy. We also had our parents' wrath to contend with. In those days, it wasn't a case of your parents grounding you—they would *kill* you!

We didn't have the privilege of attending a class to discuss sex or finding a counselor to help us through it; we simply didn't do it. In fact, it wasn't something we even thought about much because the opportunities weren't there. For one thing, our parents stayed up until our dates left. Sometimes my mother even walked my boyfriend to the door! "Bye, Ray! Don't let the cat in when you leave. Drive carefully and thank your mom for the yellow tomatoes."

About the only hugging and kissing we did was in cars. In the fifties, cars were our drugs! All we thought and talked about. Who had one? What color was it? How fast would it go and how many people could it hold? Some guys—rarely girls—were lucky enough to borrow the family car occasionally, and a few actually owned one. In those days, a teenager's car was always packed like a jar of olives.

I still love to get into a car that's been closed up overnight and take that first deep breath. If it were possible to have bottled the car smells of my youth, you could blindfold me and I'd pass the sniffing test—tell you which bottle held the smell of the interior of Ray's pink and black Ford, identify that of Gary's yellow convertible, and without a doubt, know the distinctive smell of Harold's Jeep. I have good memories of cars packed full of laughing teenagers. I also have memories of long, lingering kisses in the backseat, interrupted by teeth crashing together because of those bumpy West Virginia roads.

When I became a college freshman, my high school naivete faded rapidly. One of my first college dates was a tall, dark, handsome music major who gave me the impression that I should feel fortunate to be his choice for the evening. He didn't even kiss me; he went straight for the breasts!

My exit line was, "Okay, Columbus, you've discovered enough!" I made the mistake of telling my daughters about this experience once when we were discussing sex and they never forgot it. We still say those words and laugh.

That experience awakened an uneasy feeling in me. Having someone touch my breasts was worse than having seventh-grade boys look at them.

Later I learned that breasts were for admiring and caressing— a satisfying part of the lovemaking process. Then when I'd begun to accept and enjoy my breasts, one was cut off.

How could I not worry that my husband would reject me— think of me as not being whole or sexy? In the hospital I could pull the robes and bed jackets tightly around me, but coming home was a different story.

The first night I went into the dark closet to put on my gown. I pulled out a beautiful floor-length one with a lacy built-in bra and quickly stuffed the left side with socks. I looked in the mirror as I stepped from the closet. *Not bad*, I thought. *Not bad at all.* With a flair I got into my side of the bed. Wayne smiled.

With no hesitation at all he took me in his arms and made love to me, cautiously but passionately. That night an unspoken agreement went into effect between the two of us; for the next year, the nightgown stayed on during lovemaking. I chose to be private about my body and he respected my decision. Not long before my reconstructive surgery I showed him my scar. He reached out and touched it and looked into my eyes.

"I'll bet you'll be glad to get that fixed," he said and turned back to his book. I can honestly say my mastectomy didn't threaten the intimacy of our marriage. If anything, it made us closer.

Every case is not like mine. I know of several men who physically walked away from their wives after a mastectomy. I know some who walked away emotionally. Women ask, "How can this surgery *not* affect our lovemaking? How can I go along as though nothing is wrong?" Men ask, "How can I show her it's okay, that I don't want it to affect our sex lives?" Men sometimes ask more questions than women: "Shall I pretend it never happened? Should we laugh? Should we cry?"

A very good place to get answers to questions like these is the American Cancer Society's A New Beginning program, which meets regularly to give the breast cancer patient information and emotional support.

Husbands, daughters, and friends are invited and often come. There is usually a program or speaker; however the real purpose of the group is to meet the woman where she is, at whatever stage of emotion, and be there for her.

Because of my busy schedule, I've attended only a couple of times. Both times I intended to duck in and out, simply to hear the speaker; both times I was pulled into the camaraderie and spirit of the group.

The first time I attended, the meeting was led by a woman named Josie, young, with beautiful, black, almost iridescent skin. I thought to myself, *This woman's never had a bad day in her life. She's being paid to do this; she's a staff member.*

Josie opened the meeting by suggesting we get acquainted. "We'll go around the room, tell our names and where we are right now in our cancer journey. First of all, I'm Josie, and it's been almost seven years since I had a modified radical mastectomy. I had fourteen bad lymph nodes. I was twenty-four when it happened and didn't know a thing about cancer till it hit home. I thought I was going to die. Then I said, 'No, I've always thought positively—you're halfway there if you can think positively—I can lick this. I have the best doctors in the world, and my belief in God is strong.' I just kept saying, 'You can lick it!' But it wasn't easy.

"At the same time I was taking chemotherapy, I was taking radiation—upstairs for chemo, downstairs for radiation—day after day! I had a year of chemo and thirty radiation treatments. Five years later I had reconstruction and now I'm well and healthy." She glowed!

Each woman in the first row stood and told her name and the status of her battle with cancer. Some had been cancer free for years; some were in treatment and hanging onto the hope that they, like Josie, would lick it! In the second row a woman, spoke her name and burst into tears. We waited for her to regain her composure.

"I thought I was well. I did everything they told me to do, but I've just had a recurrence. It's back. My cancer's back!" She buried her head in her hands.

We waited in uncomfortable silence, punctuated only by loud, gut-wrenching sobs. Then (the image will be in my mind forever) the tall, stately Josie moved across the room and knelt by the side of this devastated woman and with her beautiful hands stroked her face and wiped her tears. The meeting came to a dead halt. The most important thing at that moment was not to hear a speaker, see a film, or listen to a tape, but to comfort. As long as the tears fell—and it seemed an eternity—Josie's glistening, tender hands wiped them away.

I'll never forget that moment. It is a strong mental image that appears every time I'm asked, "Just what *does* the American Cancer Society do?"

The question of intimacy after breast cancer often comes up at these meetings, and the volunteers are equipped to help. I asked Donna, another American Cancer Society volunteer, "You've talked to a lot of women, and men too. What gets couples through this mastectomy ordeal with their sexual relationships intact?"

"I think if you start out with a close, intimate relationship you have a better chance. On the other hand, I've heard of it working the other way; couples having a tenuous relationship can be brought together by the trauma of a mastectomy. I guess there's no pat answer."

As for me and my husband, we found that humor greatly helped ease the intimacy problem. Often what we couldn't talk about, we could laugh about. After my first program of chemotherapy, which began in the hospital, Wayne surprised me with a trip to Puerto Rico—one of the most wonderful, intimate times we ever spent together.

We stayed in an elegant hotel. Every day we got up late, ate a leisurely breakfast, sunned by the ocean, walked, talked, took naps, dressed for dinner, and strolled the hotel "people watching"—one of our favorite things to do.

My husband made two comments that week that many people would think strange; but for me, they were a turning point in our postoperative relationship. They assured me that things hadn't changed between us at all. One night he bought tickets to what was described as a "Las Vegas Show" in the hotel where we were staying.

Although we weren't warned ahead of time, the dance extravaganza finale featured bare-breasted women. At first, Wayne was all eyes. Then suddenly aware of the strangeness of the circumstances, he leaned close, took my hand, and without missing a beat said, "I was just counting . . . they all have two! Let's go."

On another day, I teasingly asked him, "Do you think you can love me now for my *mind* instead of my body?" Without flinching, he answered, "Honey, if I'd seen as much of your mind as I have your body, I'd be able to tell you!"

To some, those responses might seem unkind or even cruel. To me, they ensured our sense of humor was intact.

Recently, I was reacquainted with a distant relative at a funeral. Other than playing together once or twice—she lived in Columbus, Ohio; I lived in Charleston, West Virginia—the thing I remembered most vividly about Janice was that I, as a child, wore her hand-me-down clothes. Every year or so a box came and there would be five or six beautiful, almost-new dresses.

After the funeral we went back to my uncle's home for dinner. In the course of the afternoon, Janice shared with me the fact she too had had breast cancer. With a twinkle in her eye, she told me she wore a homemade prosthesis—her experience with store-bought ones was unsatisfactory. She explained how she had come up with the ingenious idea of filling a piece of nylon stocking with birdseed and stuffing it in the pocket she had sewn in her bra.

"Works great," she said; then with a slight blush, she added, "Tom says he can look in the sky and tell when I'm comin' by the great trail of birds following me!" I knew by the humor that Tom, like Wayne, had helped his wife feel comfortable about a very touchy subject.

Many women have shared with me their first sexual experience after a mastectomy. Some tell of renewed romantic interest; others tell stories best described as nightmares. I went to visit Marlene, at the request of a mutual friend. Marlene, who was unmarried, was belligerent about the subject of reconstructive surgery.

"Why should I have my breasts rebuilt just to make some man happy?" she said. "When I meet someone, he'll just have to get used to it!"

One day she called to tell me she'd gone away on a singles weekend; after getting chummy with one of the male attendees—and drunk in the process—she ended up in his bed. The man, reaching for a breast and finding instead a thick scar, literally jumped from the bed in horror, practically throwing her to the floor in the process. Marlene didn't learn her lesson; she repeated the experience several times over.

The last time I spoke with her she said, "I've had some real bad experiences with sex." It didn't occur to her that a one-night stand isn't the place to find a sympathetic mate.

Kitty came to visit me right after my mastectomy and was appalled that I would consider "putting myself under the knife" again to have reconstructive surgery. "I had a double mastectomy years ago and my husband loves me just like I am. We've had no problems, . . . no problems at all." She brought the subject up several times during her visit. Years later I hired a decorator who had worked with Kitty. I explained I'd had a bad year—having a mastectomy, chemo, and reconstructive surgery—and wanted to spruce up the living room a bit.

"Be glad you had reconstructive surgery," he said. "I work with this woman named Kitty who decided against it. She and her husband had trouble from day one and it hasn't ended yet!"

Both Marlene and Kitty were unrealistic and had adopted an almost combative attitude toward their circumstances. I'm glad that's not the norm. Donna, my friend from the American Cancer Society, tells me the "unofficial" survey at A New Beginning says most relationships tend to improve during this life-shattering experience; my own unofficial survey seems to agree.

A young teacher told me she'd had small breasts to begin with so it hardly made a difference. Later her husband told me the same story. Both told of a new, deeper intimacy than they'd had before; their eyes told me this was true.

Not long ago a thirty-seven-year-old woman called from California. We'd never met, but I've discovered sometimes it's much easier to talk to a stranger miles away than it is to talk to a friend or family member. After a mastectomy Beverly is in the process of finishing up her chemotherapy. She has two small children and her husband is out of work. She confided that her relationship with her husband, which was tenuous before the mastectomy, was now quite strong. She has no plans for reconstructive surgery.

Joanie did as I did—chose not to let her mate see her naked body after her mastectomy. She told me she kept her body covered, wore teddies or gowns, and locked the bathroom door whenever she bathed. One day she forgot to lock the door and Will walked in. Quickly she tried to cover herself with the wash-cloth as she begged him to get out! Undeterred, he moved to the edge of the tub, knelt, took her in his arms, and said, "I love *you*, not your breasts. When will you understand?"

"He cried and I cried and it all ran together ... *my* tears, *his* tears, and the bathwater!" she told me. What a wonderful way to wash away the fear and uncertainty!

When It Rains, It Pours

WHEN IT RAINS, IT POURS." Noah's wife said that! It was the thirty-ninth day she'd been on that creaky ark with all those sneezing, sniveling relatives. Everyone was out of clothes; the ones she'd washed five days before were still wet. She was down to the last of the food supplies and she'd had all she could stand of restless, smelly, wet animals. She didn't dare turn her back for fear of being kicked by a kangaroo, swatted by a lion, or stepped on by a rhinoceros. She'd been a healthy woman when she stepped on that boat, now she was as claustrophobic and paranoid as she could get, with a permanent case of vertigo to boot!

Noah's wife never realized it, but her words caught on like loincloths after the fall of man. All through early biblical history people repeated it. Sarah said to Abraham, "Abraham, it seems to me, when it rains, it pours. Does it seem that way to you?" And Lot said to Lot's wife, "Wife, did you ever notice, when it rains, it pours?"

Read Genesis if you want to read about major life trauma. These people were not living balanced, healthy lives! They were not in good relationships. Most of them were living out of suitcases, traveling on donkeys, and sleeping in tents, which is bound to predispose a family to dysfunction. Each time they stopped they built an altar. Compulsion if I ever saw it. Maybe an "applauded" addiction! Just learning about circumcision for the first time must have been a jolt to the psychological persona!

It was a driven society full of risktakers, going to war at the drop of a hat and having to survive all those physiological illnesses without a PPO, HMO, or Convenient Care Center. Friends and family members were dying left and right and yet they were without the benefit of grief and anger books. And famines were apparently endured without the help of rock concerts, foreign aid, or Willie Nelson!

Check out that first book in the Bible if you think things are messed up today—a wife pretending to be her husband's sister, daughters having babies by their father, people being tricked into marriages, a woman turning to salt, angels fighting off homosexuals, unexplainable dreams, a brother killing his brother, brothers selling a brother, and more—strong indications of a need for reparenting due to negative messages as a result of generational, relational fallout!

Down through history when the load became almost too heavy to bear, when everything bad seemed to happen at once, people have said it. Mrs. Noah's catchy slogan was even picked up later by a salt company. Folks still say it today: "When it rains, it pours!"

I sometimes visit a woman with breast cancer and she tells me her insurance lapsed a month before her illness, or that her son had a car accident, or her unmarried daughter is pregnant, or her husband just lost his job—sometimes all of the above!

"If it were *just* cancer, I could handle it," she tells me, "but it's all these other things happening at the same time!" When it comes to problems, it truly does seem they arrive in torrents. It was true for me.

The year of my mastectomy and chemotherapy, my downpour centered on my mother's illness. I knew she wondered where I was, why I hadn't come during her most recent setback. I called her each day, with the exception of the day of my surgery, and tried to cheer her up. I could barely hear her voice as she lapsed in and out of consciousness.

As soon as the doctor would let me, I made arrangements to fly to West Palm Beach where Mother's husband, Jim, would pick me up and take me to Boca Raton Hospital. I hoped to spend the time with my mother, even planned to stay the night in her room. I didn't want to spend time with Jim.

I felt that given the chance, he would manipulate me; I knew the pattern from past experience. He would take me to the hospital and stand impatiently on one foot, then the other, while I visited with Mother; then after a short time he'd suggest we leave so she could rest. He'd take me to *his* choice of restaurant (greasy), to the grocery store, to church if there was a service, or he would suggest we swim or visit his friends. If I wanted to see Mother again in the evening, he would give me a short no-questions-asked answer: "It's not necessary!"

Before my trip, Wayne called ahead to pave the way. "Please take Sue to the hospital and leave her there. She wants to spend the time with her mother. Don't insist she go out to eat. Let her pick up something at the hospital, and please don't involve her in any decisions; she's not up to it." Jim was planning to move Mother to a nursing home and had suggested we spend our time shopping for the right facility. My brothers were both on call for decision making.

As I flew south, the knot in my stomach was not from my medication or worry for Mother, but from the dread of dealing with Jim.

Walking out through the jetway, I could see his smiling face eagerly waiting. A pang of guilt ran through me as I thought of the pain this poor man had suffered. His first wife had died a long, slow death from cancer, and now he was losing Mother, whom he called "the love of his life."

My guilt pang didn't last long. Before we were even on the expressway, Jim began: "We have a lot of work to do, many decisions to be made. I hope you're in no hurry to get to the hospital. I have several appointments lined up." I gulped.

"We need to plan the funeral while you're here," he continued as he pulled the car off the road and into a parking lot. I wondered why we were stopping in front of a large white house. *Probably a restaurant*, I thought. The big funeral home sign didn't register. My brain was numb.

"Dear [he always called me that], I've picked a casket. It's quite lovely. It has a peach lining. Your mother would like it. She's always liked peach. I want you to see it . . . approve it."

Like a zombie I got out of the car. With his hand under my elbow, he swept me up the steps. The door opened, automatically it seemed, and there stood Lurch of *The Addams Family* TV fame, except his suit was white instead of black. His smile was the same.

Lurch led us to a large room full of caskets—all colors, all sizes, all prices. Jim took my arm and guided me across the room, stopping in front of a pale gray number with a peach lining. Sure enough, it was the perfect choice! Just what Mother would have chosen herself, and sure enough, I behaved just as Mother would have wanted me to.

I didn't scream profane words or scratch out Jim's eyes or knee Lurch in the groin. Instead, I smiled sweetly, ran my hands over the satin (probably acetate) lining, admired the styling, nodded my head in agreement and said that yes, it was probably the loveliest casket I'd ever seen and perfect for my mother. Just perfect!

Perhaps it is the right thing to do, plan for Mother's death, I thought as we drove away; *after all, it's only natural, Jim would want me to have a say in the decisions*. Little did I imagine it would be nine long months before we would actually need that casket!

But right then, nothing would do but that we stop for lunch. After lunch—a lunch I didn't want—he took me to the hospital and I tried to ignore him as I visited with Mother. As I had anticipated, he stood on one foot, then the other. She was barely conscious, but I knew she felt my touch; her questioning eyes met mine as I talked to her. Jim was in a hurry. He had things he wanted to do and I was part of his plan.

We visited three nursing homes. At the third, I discovered he'd already given them a deposit for the first month! I hoped against hope the actual move would take place after I was back in Nashville, but that was not to be. I soon found that Jim's plan was to move Mother the very next day so I could help him.

"It's not necessary," was Jim's response when I asked to be taken to see Mother that evening on our way home from dinner. "What you need is a good night's sleep, dear."

I knew him well enough to know that his answer was final and making a scene would give him the opportunity to condescend to me: "Oh, you poor thing! You *are* upset! You really do need a good night's sleep!"

I'd bitten my lip almost bloody to keep from speaking my mind throughout the day. I'd made it through the greasy dinner and I'd kept my mouth shut when he vetoed a visit to the hospital, but the next thing that happened made me lose it completely!

We no sooner were in the door of the condominium, than he turned to me and said, "Your mother won't be needing her clothes anymore. I want you to go through her closet and get things ready for me to take to the resale shop tomorrow."

I quietly followed him to Mother's closet; when I saw the rows of familiar dresses, I came unglued. I reached for the first dress, pulled it out—hanger and all—and flung it in his face shouting: "I bought this!" Dress after dress flew through the air. "I bought this! And this! And this!" Then I turned to him, and with my finger practically up his nose, I spat out, "You . . . aren't . . . getting . . . rid . . . of . . . *my* . . . mother's . . . clothes!" I saw a glimmer of terror in his eyes. "I'll pack them and take them to Nashville, but you're not selling *anything!*"

The next day, we moved Mother from the hospital to the nursing home. It seemed more than I could bear to see her poor, pain-racked body tousled from bed to stretcher to ambulance and to bed again.

After she was settled in her new surroundings, I insisted Jim leave us alone. I picked Mother's shrunken, cadaver-like body up in my arms and held her and rocked her. Her eyes never left mine, questioning. Suddenly we were both crying, our tears mingling and our bodies shaking with great heaves and soundless sobs. I didn't dare open my mouth for fear of blurting out the truth— that I too had cancer, and that I knew what it was like to be dying. Perhaps she knew. Sometimes mothers just know!

Jim continued to be difficult, expecting everything to be on his terms. Toward the end of my visits, I discovered a way to deal with him. Why hadn't I thought of it sooner? I found that if I could make him angry right off the bat, he would punish me by ignoring me. It was easy once I'd begun, and I could use the fact that I was heavily medicated as an excuse to be mean. "Just can't help myself. Chemo makes you mean!"

He hated smoking with a vengeance and I would argue in favor of it even though I hated it too. He disliked one of Mother's friends, describing her as stupid; so I would invite her along when we went out.

I learned to poke around and stall and make him late for his golf game or to ask him to wait while I ran into the shopping center for stockings and came out an hour later. I insisted my sick stomach could only tolerate a certain restaurant. It happened they served pasta instead of potatoes as a side dish; Jim's evening meal wasn't complete without potatoes.

"Whoever heard of a restaurant without potatoes," he'd complain to the waitress. Then he would give me the silent treatment for the rest of the evening. I'm embarrassed to say I loved it!

My last visit to Florida before Mother's death was peaceful. Wayne insisted I rent a car so as not to depend on Jim. Why hadn't we thought of *that* sooner? For the most part, Jim left me alone.

I sat by Mother's side and talked to her about my childhood and told her what a good mother she was. I told her about our beautiful little Cara Jane and reminisced about Daddy and our cats. Occasionally she smiled; most of the time, however, her eyes were glassy.

One day while I was there, old friends from Charleston came to visit. The few people who had visited before barely glanced at her, spoke quietly to me, and left as quickly as possible. Not Bill and Sylvia! They ran to Mother's side, took her hands in theirs, and spoke directly to her. "Mary Jane, we're so excited for you! You're going home! You're going to heaven! You're going to see Maynard." My daddy. "Oh, tell him hello for us! Mary Jane, you'll be well . . . it will be so wonderful."

Suddenly I was no longer sad. Mother wasn't dying. She was going home. And yes, she would be well! She would see Daddy! It *would* be wonderful!

Not long before Mother's death, my oncologist changed my treatment. He explained that the new protocol was more debilitating than the one I had been on and that it would most likely lower my white blood count and my resistance. I'd already experienced times when my white count was so low treatment had to be postponed. Now it would be certain to happen again. He warned about possible side effects—mouth sores, infection, and loss of hair.

"We'll give you these new drugs as long as your system can tolerate them," he said. "Then we'll go back to the original program." I remember that one drug was called Vinblastin. After two or three treatments, I thought, *Its name serves it well! It certainly is blastin' me!*

What hair I had left turned from blonde to an ugly, dull shade of steel gray. Once again my friends at the beauty shop stood by to help; but despite innumerable hours there, my hair refused to respond. Pat, Hazel, Brenda, and Ann couldn't help my *hair*, but they always managed to lift my *spirit* and make me laugh at my dilemma.

All of my body odors intensified with an added whiff of chemical. "Can't you smell that?" I'd ask my husband. "How can you bear to be near me?" He swore he didn't notice.

A couple of times I hallucinated. One night at home I felt smothered; I wrapped myself in a quilt and walked out on the sundeck to get a breath of fresh air. It was a clear, cool, starry night, and I stretched out on the chaise lounge, pulling the quilt up around my chin. I lay there for a long time looking into the sky. Up, up, up through the stars.

This must be what it feels like to be a druggie, I thought, aware of the effects of the strong medicine. *I've heard about it, but never experienced it. This must be what it feels like to trip out.*

Up, up, up through the stars. Then I'm floating, like a combination of swimming and flying. The stars seem to be over and under and all around me. I can look down and see myself lying in the lounge chair; however when I look more closely, I see myself not as an adult but as a child—little more than a baby. I am lying on my back on a rag rug in the kitchen of my childhood home on Sixth Street in Charleston. I can see right into the laughing faces of my parents and their friends, Margarite and Capey. I can hear them speaking.

"Capey, how are you doing on that television you're building?" my mother asks.

"There are parts everywhere—all over the house," Margarite whines. I can see the deep pockmarks on her otherwise pretty face.

"I've never seen a television *work*," my daddy says, "but if anyone can build one that works, Capey, you can." They all look down at me, in my lounge chair or on the rag rug on the floor. Wherever I am!

I am holding a little pimento cheese glass full of water. Mother, Daddy, Margarite, and Capey are standing above me trying their best to convince me that drinking water while lying on my back is a bad idea.

"You can't do it, Suz," my daddy is saying, "you'll choke." I pay no attention. I tip the glass to my mouth. Water, instead of gushing over me, *sprinkles* down on me—on my face . . . in my eyes . . . on my hair.

Suddenly I am back on the chaise lounge on the deck and rain is falling on my face.

Another time, during the day, I lay on my back on the sundeck looking into the sky. Up, up, up, perhaps to infinity. Again my sensory perception was intensified by the drugs.

I can hear the echo of a voice.

"Sue, you are wearing me out!" It's one of my great-aunts—Aunt Annie or Aunt Maggie (they both sound the same). "Lie still and hush. Do you hear me?"

Up, up, up. I can see the picture that hangs above the daybed in the old home place in southern Ohio. Aunt Maggie and Aunt Annie have told me I need to rest because I'm wearing them out. I've looked up into the picture at least a million times; this time, though, I'm experiencing the eerily familiar sensation of both swimming and flying. Right into the picture I'm going. Up the gray fieldstone steps with hollyhocks and snapdragons and roses all around me. When I get to the top and walk under the archway of roses, there is a playhouse. If I go inside, there will be a winding stairway like the one in the old home place where my aunts rarely let me play. "Too drafty," they say.

Still I decide to play on the stairway in the playhouse. It will be the multilevel Hollywood apartment house for the fake paper dolls I cut from the Montgomery Ward catalog.

"She'll catch her death in that cold, drafty stairway," I hear one of the aunts say.

I'm looking out the window of my playhouse and I see, not the child on the daybed, but the adult me who wonders momentarily if she's caught her death from playing on the cold, drafty stairway. Otherwise why would she feel so wretched?

I pull myself out of the lounge chair and go into the house, knowing that the incident really happened—both incidents, in fact—when I was a very small child. The drugs were responsible for the return of these memories.

What strikes me today is the vividness and intensity of those hallucinations and the feeling that I was understanding "truth" in life-shaking proportions. It makes me understand why a person can be bamboozled by mind-altering drugs. Under their influence, a relatively insignificant memory or thought can manifest itself in monstrous proportions.

One day I sat in my office wondering how much longer I could go on with my treatment, especially this new, more aggressive protocol. I wanted to continue as long as possible, but I could tell it was taking its toll. It was midafternoon on Friday; I longed for the day to be over so I could "crash" for the weekend. All of a sudden my breathing became labored.

"Abby," I called to my secretary, "I'm feeling really weird . . . as though my breathing is being cut off."

"Let's get you to the couch," she said, guiding me in that direction.

"I know this sounds crazy, but I feel as though I'm smothering. I'm . . . dying," I said as I fell back against the pillows. I was blacking out. Abby pulled off my shoes and began to rub my feet with all her might.

"No, you aren't going to die; you aren't." Over and over she called my name: "Sue! Sue! Come back! Come back!" Finally I began to breathe normally again. I sat up and rubbed my arms. My skin was as cold as ice and ghastly white.

"I looked death right in the face, Abby. Right smack in the face!" I could see that she believed me, but I did feel rather foolish.

A little while later as I walked into the house from work, the phone was ringing. It was my brother Joe calling to say Mother was dead. I should have felt relief. The last time I'd seen her, her body had shriveled to nothing; her bones looked as though they would burst through her skin; her eyes were vacant. I'd prayed for her to die.

Why was I sobbing? Why was my body shaking, from the bottoms of my feet to the top of my head? Why was there a jarring pain in my skull that felt like a jabbing knife? My mind played connect the dots. *Of course! The cancer has metastasized in my brain. My mother is dead! My mother is dead and her funeral will simply be a rehearsal for my own!* My family tried to comfort me, but I couldn't be comforted.

That night in bed I relived the experience in the office. I rewound and played it again as if on a tape recorder. I wanted to unlock the mystery. Why did I feel as though I was smothering at the time of Mother's death? Another one of life's inexplicable scenarios. I never slept. I never shut my eyes.

The next day, as we pulled into the parking lot of the big white funeral home in Boca Raton, I wondered if they had sold Mother's casket.

Nine months is a long time to hold one, I thought. We walked into the dimly lit parlor. How beautiful she looked—not sick at all—dressed in the peach-colored chiffon dress I'd bought her so long ago, lying in the peach-lined casket.

That night I sat on Mother's bedroom floor and sorted through her keepsakes. Not much was left. She had already divided the important things among my brothers and me. There were newspaper clippings and her high school yearbook, her wedding book, and beautifully penned obituaries of her mother and grandmother—and pictures. I looked closely at each photograph. Who were these sepia-toned people? I reached for what appeared to be pages torn from an old family Bible, records listing births and baptisms, weddings and deaths. As I noted the dates, I couldn't help wondering what went between. There were no clues. What were *their* fears? *Their* disappointments? *Their* joys? What would *my* descendants know about me?

Mother's funeral was funny. Nothing related to her or her life. The elderly minister centered his message around the story of a yellow dog named Caesar. It wasn't even an interesting story, only that the dog had died and been sadly mourned by his human family. Caesar had been placed in the ground forever.

"If our dear friend did not know God," he motioned toward Mother's casket, "then her life was in vain, nothing more than this yellow dog named Caesar." I giggled under my breath. Surely one of my brothers would stand and challenge what was being said. Would they let him get away with it, allow him to drone on and on and never mention our mother or our grief?

I'll stand up myself. I'll tell him. I would tell him about her deep abiding faith and her special gift of hospitality. How she had opened our home to dozens of missionary families; how rarely a Sunday meal passed without someone being invited so they wouldn't "have to eat alone."

Didn't he know what an inspiration she had been to us in life ... *and* in death? What about our grief and mourning? Did he have no words of comfort to offer? Just as I was poised and ready to stand, I thought, *Of course not! I can't do that, because it isn't really happening! I'm on another of my wild drug trips.*

What happened next brought me back to reality in a hurry. I saw my brothers exchange brief glances and saw Jon give me a knowing look. I could feel my husband's body shudder slightly in laughter. Dear God, I was sane! I *was* sane!

When the girls were little and we heard a male singer with a deep voice and an exaggerated vibrato, Mindy would lower her voice, get a very ominous look on her face, and say, "Liiisssten to the vaaampiire siiinngerr!" Then we would all sing like "vampire singers" and laugh like fools. Mother enjoyed it more than anyone.

Sure enough, Jim had asked a real-life vampire singer to perform at Mother's funeral. It wouldn't have surprised me in the least had she sat up and laughed. It was all the four of us could do—Joe, Jon, Wayne, and me—to keep straight faces. In the car, on the way to the cemetery, we were able to laugh about Caesar and the vampire singer; it helped to ease the emptiness.

Mother had joked, "Bury me in Florida and I'll come back to haunt you!" We undoubtedly were in for a double dose of haunting. We were burying her not only in Florida, but in *Lantana*, Florida, home of the *National Enquirer!* Jim had his way again. I didn't know it at the time, but the graves were one on top of the other, bunk-bed style; and Jim, of course, would eventually be on top.

At the grave site I quietly spoke to the old minister, who perhaps had preached too many funerals in a part of the country where folks go to live out their final days and where death is such a common occurrence.

"Please say *something* about our mother," I pleaded. He put aside his notes and did what I had asked.

We stood huddled together, not against cold, but against the unfamiliar tropical air that tasted like salt. I glanced down and saw stubby, coarse grass growing up through sand. Above me tall stalks of palm trees flared minimally against a too blue, too clear sky—fine for a resort playground, but not suitable to shade a mother's grave.

My eyes scanned the markers with their unfamiliar names. Why couldn't Mother be buried beside Daddy on that beautiful plot of earth in the West Virginia hills next to Mae and Elmer and where the family marker was already in place?

Celebrating Your Faith

I BELIEVE IN GOD *the Father almighty,*
  Maker of Heaven and Earth,
  And in Jesus Christ His only Son our Lord

The Apostles' Creed. We often say it in unison in our church services. I like repeating it until it rings in my head like the words to a familiar song. And I like the *exacts* of it—kind of like my husband telling me about the car.

"Have your car serviced. Do it on a Tuesday when they aren't busy. Speak directly with the service manager. Take this list with you so they don't miss anything. Charge it to Visa and pick it up before 4:30 so you miss the busy time."

Okay! Now that you've explained it, I can handle it. I like that approach much better than when he mutters, "Car needs serviced." I can ignore the mutterings for weeks on end.

Before my illness, I knew the basics—that I was God's child and that I would be in heaven when I died—beyond that it was mutterings. Now that death was looming, it seemed prudent to figure out exactly what I could really stake my life on.

I grew up in a fundamentalist church where repeating the Apostles' Creed would not have been an acceptable part of the service. In fact, we steered clear of anything that could be thought of as *high church.* We had no particular order to our service, for fear we might not be led by the Holy Spirit. We were proud that our money went to missions, not stained glass and steeples; we had no beautiful edifice because we weren't hung up on bricks and mortar. Perhaps we *were* hung up, though, on not being hung up.

Once I attended a magnificent Episcopal church with my friend Patsy. How I admired the architecture, the stone facade and imposing archways. Afterward I hungered for stained glass, dark polished wood, real pews, and repetitions that seemed to ring with beauty and authority.

My parents' church began in a little Christian bookstore on the mezzanine of the old People's Store (later Stone and Thomas) in Charleston, West Virginia. A small group of employees began a Bible study; as the group grew, they found bigger places to meet—a storefront, an automobile showroom, and then a large house, which was gutted and remodeled to provide Sunday school classrooms and a meeting room. The chairs in the meeting room were nice thick theater seats that came from a salvage store.

"If those seats could talk," laughed one of my mother's friends, "we'd get an earful for sure."

"They've seen some sin in their time, I'd say," answered another.

As a child I tried to imagine all the things those chairs might say if they *could* talk, but came up short since I didn't know that much about sin.

Eventually we did build a regular church building, not of stone with graceful archways, but of cinder block. Even though it had no steeple or stained glass, I did breathe a sigh of relief that I could finally invite my friends for Bring Your Neighbor Sunday to somewhere besides an automobile showroom!

"God said it, I believe it, and that settles it for me." That seemed to be the answer for everything! Now I think it really was a pat answer that excused folks from thinking. My church would not have dealt with God's coincidences, like the mysterious rose petals scattered up the hill at the moment of Daddy's death. And our very Christianity would have been in question if we admitted that sometimes we felt as though our prayers weren't getting any higher than the ceiling, which is what I felt when Mother was sick.

Judgments that I didn't understand were often made. For instance, a couple from church had a car accident Sunday morning. "What can you expect?" I heard someone say. "Joe and Gertie went for a drive instead of going to church. That's why they had that wreck!"

Obviously, if they had been inside the church building, they wouldn't have wrecked their car, but wasn't the implication that the accident was a form of God's judgment? I wondered about the dear old lady they called a saint who never missed church in her life but whose house burned to the ground. The inconsistencies were great.

What about the Sunday school superintendent who was considered "godly" and whose wife, on the other hand, was a "real doozy—all that dyed black hair and no *zeal* for the church." The two of them went on vacation, had a terrible car accident and she was killed. He recovered and went on to marry someone who had *zeal* for the church equal to his own! Did God do him a favor? I couldn't explain it, and questions weren't encouraged.

The service itself, most of all the music, was a child's delight. It was unpredictable and fun. Even though we sang songs from the hymnbook, we almost always sang choruses too.

Deep and wide,
Deep and wide,
There's a fountain flowing deep and wide.

I liked that song because I didn't have to "Sit still, Sue! Sit still, Sue! Sit still!" Everyone did the hand motions, even the old people.

Better yet, I liked the chorus,

Hallelu, Hallelu, Hallelu, Hallelujah;
Praise ye the Lord!

First time through in unison, second time men and boys on the "Hallelu" and women on the "praise ye the Lord." Then it really got exciting! We popped up and sat down in turns. Men up for "Hallelu" and women for "praise ye the Lord." Up and down. By this time, if things weren't totally out of hand, the song leader would say, "Let's see who can sing the loudest." We kids, at least, would scream our parts at the top of our lungs.

Testimony time was an important part of almost every service; I could almost predict who would testify. Mr. Plumley would stand up and hop around on his one and only leg and talk about the "saving grace of God"; but even at a young age, I knew that anything Mr. Plumley said should be discredited because he chewed tobacco!

Without a doubt Charlie would testify. Charlie's story was always the same: doctors had predicted he would die before he was twelve. Here he was eighteen . . . then twenty . . . then twenty-two. Last I heard, Charlie was still alive; in his near-sixty years, he has touched thousands of people with his outgoing personality . . . *and* Christian testimony! In those days, though, the kids called him *crazy* and said that someday his oversized head would just explode—pop all over the place. I didn't want to be sitting by him in church when it happened!

Some people talked about a life of sin. I didn't know one thing about a life of sin; I did know, however, that sometimes it had to do with divorce, and divorce rated right up there with tobacco when it came to sin! It seemed reasonable that God might not like the smell of tobacco. I didn't like it much either. It also seemed reasonable that He didn't like divorce. Even as a child, I knew divorce made people unhappy and divided families and friends.

I even thought that possibly God did get bored with a "form" of worship—same old rigamarole, same old prayers, same old words over and over, service after service, week after week. It even made sense that God didn't need stained glass and steeples.

I remember being full of questions when I was a child and even more so as a teenager. For instance, "How do I know the virgin birth of Christ is true?" But even more important to me than whether or not the virgin birth was true—God said it, I believe it, and that settles it—was the issue of wearing makeup. "Barn paint," our pastor called it!

When I was a young teen two strikingly beautiful women began attending our church—dramatic hairdos, beautiful clothes, and plenty of makeup—exactly the way I secretly wanted to look when I grew up.

Things will change now, I thought. *Everyone will see that women are much more beautiful wearing makeup than with colorless faces.*

The church women didn't change, but the two women did. Soon someone set them straight and told them the Lord wanted them to be godly. That meant the Lord couldn't possibly be happy with them until they stopped wearing barn paint and toned down their hair and wardrobes too. They did and, in my opinion, looked awful! I would have been willing to bet the Lord would have been just as happy with them wearing makeup, but at my church we didn't bet either!

As I got older I wore makeup. Often, when I was in high school no one showed up to play the piano for church. When that happened the song leader slipped up to me at the last minute and quietly asked me to go into the restroom and wash off my makeup, so I could play.

Maybe someday I'll be old and "godly" and I'll renounce my lipstick and rouge, I thought, *but for now I'll paint the barn!*

Everyone in that congregation carried a Bible as if it were glued to them. Had someone shown up without a Bible, it would have been a more obvious omission than showing up without shoes. And they *used* those Bibles! When the pastor referred to a Scripture reference, you could hear the rustle of pages turning like leaves blowing in the wind.

Everyone, big and small, old and young, was encouraged to *memorize* Scripture. Children were bribed to learn Bible verses with free trips to camp and candy bars, and I would do anything for candy. Then or now!

I won a whole box of Mallow Cup candy bars at camp once; the thought still nauseates me. I ate all of them, one right after another, in the backseat of the church's panel truck, traveling down a winding West Virginia highway. I don't need to tell you "... the rest of the story!"

We not only memorized the verses but we knew the references which we called a "street address." "Genesis 1:1," our teacher would call out, and the first kid to jump out of his seat and begin quoting got a point. The competition became so serious that we held meets with other churches and someone's dad invented an electronic contraption to prove whose bottom left the chair seat first. I loved the excitement, but I doubt I understood the true meaning of those verses. Neither did I know how to apply them to my life—*or* my impending death.

As I dealt with cancer, hardly a day went by that I didn't think about dying. It seemed I was always hearing someone make statements such as "He fought a dreadful battle with cancer." *And lost*, I'd add under my breath. I never heard someone say, "He fought a dreadful battle with a ruptured aorta!" How could I not think of my own mortality?

I had embraced the essentials of Christianity and I was sure beyond the shadow of a doubt that when I breathed my last breath I would instantaneously be in heaven. Beyond that, though, there were so many questions, the greatest being "Why?" and followed by, "How can I deal with this on a daily basis between now and dying?"

Physically, I hated losing a body part, but I had a plan for reconstructive surgery. Spiritually I was still looking for answers—not for *dying*, but for *living*. Sometimes God sends answers in strange ways. For me they came in the form of an obscure little book. I've heard you can tell how bad your case is by how many books people bring you. Along with flowers, balloons, and fruit baskets, my friends had been sending books at such a pace I'd begun stacking them in a corner. You couldn't read that many books in a lifetime, especially *my lifetime*. I wasn't even buying green bananas!

One day a book called *The Healing Power of Christ* arrived from Carolyn, my sister-in-law. Unlike the others, this book had been around a while. It was without a jacket and stained as though someone had handled it with mayonnaise on his fingers. It was dog-eared and its pages were yellow with time.

"It's old and out of print, and I'd really like to have it back," Carolyn said when she called. "It's something I want to keep. It's meant a great deal to me."

Maybe the only reason I read it was that Carolyn wanted it back. I also knew that she would no doubt call some morning to discuss it. So right away, I leafed through the text with every intention of skimming a little here and a little there to get ready to bluff my end of the conversation.

"Episcopal Church." The words on the very first page jumped out at me. There were references to *The Book of Common Prayer*, the sacraments, and the confessions. Instead of Mary and Paul, the author referred to the Virgin Mary and Saint Paul. I could almost smell the dark polished wood of the Episcopal church in Charleston. I remembered the beauty of the sun shining through the stained glass, the singsongy chant of the priest, and the response of the congregation. I was hooked and for all the wrong reasons.

This book instantly became part of my daily routine. I felt compelled to focus on God, and the book appealed to some unexplainable need for beauty and form and organization in that focus. And yet it was something more. I didn't know what.

"Coming to God repeatedly is good," it said. At its urging, I began to repeat the Lord's Prayer often; and for the first time in my life, found meaning in its words. It became my own at times when I felt my feeble words weren't getting any higher than the ceiling. Likewise, the repetition of the Apostles' Creed caused me to take its message to heart and find comfort in being able to narrow down to the exacts. To say exactly what I believed and why.

Eventually Carolyn and I did have our discussion and I returned the book to her. Four years later when I was visiting her in California, I asked, "Do you still have that little book you loaned me when I was sick? I miss it."

"I miss it too. I have no idea what happened to it. I loaned it to someone when I was still living in Phoenix, and I don't remember who it was." She explained she'd made several calls trying to track it down.

When I returned to Nashville, my secretary and I called a number of priests, publishers, bookstores, specialists in out-of-print books, and even the Episcopal Book Club trying to track down a copy. No luck.

A year later, on the day of my five-year, cancer-free celebration, a package arrived from Carolyn. I tore open the gift wrapping and discovered the well-worn book. Inside the cover Carolyn had lovingly written:

Dearest Sue,

I know you are aware this is more than an old book. It has had a curious odyssey. First, it taught me about healing long before I knew how much I needed it personally; then later, for Webb [her son who was healed from cystic fibrosis]. It traveled through a few other hands and then came into yours. Now it is back to you, a permanent home in celebration of God's great gift to you and to your family who loves you so.

Love,
Carolyn

This profound book—this special message from God—that had been my spiritual food in the most difficult year of my life was in my hands again. I stretched out on my chaise lounge and hoped that no one would interrupt as I opened the pages.

As I'd done five years earlier, I read in no particular order, just grabbing a sentence here and a paragraph there, this time driven by excitement. Nothing jumped from the pages. Nothing at all. Then I started at the beginning, thinking I would read straight through page by page. I found insights and observations worth contemplating, but not at all the kind of stuff I would stake my life on. Not at all what I'd remembered.

Aha! Page 88. This must be it! "Coming to God is repeatedly emphasized throughout the New Testament and especially in the Lord's Prayer. Here we ask, 'Give us this day our daily bread.' We cannot store up God's grace. He wants us to come to Him continually." That had certainly helped me five years earlier.

I remembered how I prayed the Lord's Prayer over and over when I had no words of my own. In the margin, I saw that I'd made a faint pencil mark at the beginning of the sentence. My eyes backtracked to the last line of the paragraph before: " . . . him

that cometh to me I will in no wise cast out (John 6:37 KJV)."
Hmmm, I learned that as a child, I thought.

I thumbed on a few pages. "To the precise extent that we trust Him, we are enabled to live in His peace without fear for today or apprehension for the future." Yes! Yes! That helped me so when I awoke with night terrors. I practically skipped the next sentence. After all, it was *just* Scripture and I knew it by heart:

> Thou wilt keep him in perfect peace,
> whose mind is stayed on thee:
> because he trusteth in thee.

Good grief! I could even remember the street address: Isaiah 26:3!

This book didn't seem worth the reading, much less the effort we had put into finding it. Other than a few choice nuggets, it seemed boring, provincial, and not too well written. I picked it up a few times over the next week or so, read a few pages, and put it down again, shaking my head in wonder at what could possibly have made me think it held life's answers.

Like having a string around my finger, but being unable to remember why it was there, the secret of the book gnawed at my mind. Perhaps the intense chemotherapy drugs I had been taking caused me to find meaning when there really was none. Finally it came to me, like the lightbulb-over-the-head in the comics, and I ran to get the book.

Page 6: "My grace is sufficient for thee, for my strength is made perfect in weakness (2 Corinthians 12:9 KJV)."

Page 7: "I pray thee, let a double portion of thy spirit be upon me (2 Kings 2:9 KJV)." Oh, how I'd prayed for a double portion. Again on page 7: " . . . they shall possess the double: everlasting joy shall be unto them (Isaiah 61:7 KJV)."

I turned the pages. "Lo, I am with you alway, even unto the end of the world (Matthew 28:20 KJV)."

On and on, I uncovered truths that were there, not only before Emily Gardiner Neal wrote *The Healing Power of Christ*, but before the very foundation of the earth.

The secret was found at last! The mystery was a mystery no longer. The comfort and peace—the words that had empowered me to face the most overwhelming interference of my life—came from God's Word, faithfully transcribed by the author because of its application to her own life. My empowerment came from the same Scriptures that I'd been cajoled, bribed, and sometimes badgered to learn as a child in a little fundamentalist church in West Virginia.

I read on with a new eagerness. "For to me to live is Christ, and to die is gain. . . . For I am in a strait betwixt two (Philippians 1:21, 23 KJV)," and then "To day shalt thou be with me in paradise (Luke 23:43 KJV)."

Five years before, I'd read these pages that spoke of death as the final triumph for the Christian—perhaps the ultimate healing! I'd thought of my daddy then and I thought about him again now. I remembered the words he spoke on his deathbed: "It's so beautiful!" He was not going to the unknown.

"To day shalt thou be with me in paradise." What more did I need to know about death?

The Green Frog of Christmas

More than anything that year, I wanted Christmas to be what it usually was at our house—memorable. I was determined to have an eventful, rambunctious Christmas even though the chemical buildup from ten months of chemotherapy left me feeling ugly, puffy, lethargic, and full of poison. I repeatedly had to remind myself to *snap out of it!*—a favorite saying at our house.

The doctor juggled my treatment schedule so I could finish early in December—the intent being that I had a better chance for feeling better at Christmas. It comforted me to know I had only two months of chemo to go, but there was another worry I couldn't shake.

One day while waiting for the doctor I'd become restless and looked around for a magazine with which to pass the time. There was none and, finding nothing better to do, I began to rummage through his files. "If he finds his stuff rearranged, he'll never make me wait again," I reasoned. Then I spotted my own folder—my medical file—and began to read. Most of it was routine reports detailing my office visits and test results.

Toward the back of the folder, however, I discovered a letter written by my mastectomy surgeon. I read with interest. It said I wasn't a good candidate for reconstructive surgery because I probably wouldn't live that long! "Too bad," he said. "She is the type who would give great encouragement to others."

After I jump-started my pacemaker, my first thought was, *Well, Mister Cowboy Doctor, I've laughed in your face before and I'll do it again. After all, I'm still alive, eleven months later, and I believe I can make it one more month. Maybe longer.* The bravado was only skin deep; a lump formed in my throat and a knot settled in the pit of my stomach.

Maybe this IS my last Christmas, I worried. I remembered the lyrics to a love song, "If ever I would leave you, it wouldn't be in springtime." The verses that follow say it wouldn't be in fall, winter, or summer either. Maybe I'd write a verse of my own: "If ever I would leave you, it wouldn't be at Christmas; I don't want your second wife to have my manger scene from Bethlehem!"

I thought back over the fun and excitement of Christmases past—the year Wayne gave me a chocolate chess set, the time I gave him a pinball machine, the year I watched two grown men—Wayne and Jon—try to assemble a Barbie condo and never get it right.

One day several years before, Jon (who makes pickles from the cucumbers and dill from his own garden) discovered I didn't have a garlic press—powdered garlic was good enough for me—and began to taunt me.

"How can you call yourself a cook? No garlic press?" Then he would turn to whoever happened to be nearby and ask, "Can you believe this woman has no garlic press?"

Long before Christmas that year I knew there would be a garlic press under the tree. The surprise was that it was *electric* or maybe I should say pseudo-electric! Jon had gone to great trouble to attach a thick, long electrical cord with an industrial-sized plug to an ordinary garlic press. Had I plugged it in I probably would have been electrocuted on the spot!

Our family loves Christmas! We even love the last-minute shopping, decorating, package wrapping, silver polishing, and baking—the whole family in the kitchen trying recipes, friends stopping by for a few hours with their recipes and going home with a sampling of everything.

Midafternoon on Christmas Eve the celebrating begins at our house. We made a plan, which we started when Dana was a baby, and it continues to the present time: Christmas would be at our house; everyone was invited and whoever comes must *move in*—for two nights at least.

Most years, once our guests arrive, we can't get rid of them; and the frivolity continues for days, sometimes right up to New Year's. Once we get started, we can't stop—eating, playing games, working jigsaw puzzles, taking naps, watching movies, and then repeating it all over and over. Dana, Mindy, Jon, Becky, Cara, and Kirby always come, and some years the Nixons, Becky's parents. We fondly remember when our parents were alive and part of the festivities. Now we have Barry, our new son-in-law, with us.

"Trr-dition!" we sing, trilling our *R*s and mimicking the Yiddish accents of *Fiddler on the Roof*.

Tradition! We certainly have ours. One of our most famous is the "Traditional Green Frog of Christmas"!

Wayne isn't what I'd call a shopper, although he's instructed: "When I die, bury me at the mall . . . so Sue and the girls will visit me often!" He loves one type of store, however—the kind that sells kitchen gadgets. On one of his trips there, Wayne discovered a plastic ice mold in the shape of a frog, so he bought it, brought it home, and acted like a kid with a new toy.

Christmas Eve morning he took the ice mold out of the box, filled it with water, added green food coloring, stuck it in the freezer, and checked its progress regularly. "Yeah, it's freezing—the Green Frog of Christmas is freezing nicely," he said.

"We're happy for you, Daddy," Mindy answered in her most *in*sincere voice and rolled her eyes at the ceiling.

"The Green Frog of Christmas!" Dana and I mouthed the words to each other, held our stomachs, and bent over in not-too-silent laughter. Wayne was so euphoric he didn't noticed our mockery.

The "Traditional Green Frog of Christmas" was a hit from the first. Wayne waited till everyone gathered for the Christmas Eve festivities—family, friends, and neighbors. Everything was perfect—the smoked salmon with cream cheese and capers, cheese puffs, pâté and crackers, and a huge array of homemade cookies and candy.

When he had everyone's attention, he carried in the exquisite cut glass punch bowl and placed it on its fancy gilded base. There in the middle of the bright red punch sat the "Traditional Green Frog of Christmas" glistening proudly. We praised Wayne for his creative idea and workmanship and responded with affirmations, however insincere, to his "Do you like the frog? Huh? Do you like the frog?"

But the moment of glory—for both Wayne and the green frog—didn't last long. As the frog began to melt, sounds much like those of a belch—or worse—came forth from his *green-ness!* Not only that! As the green food coloring blended with the red punch the mixture took on the color of the "or worse," if you know what I mean.

We actually only celebrated the "Traditional Green Frog of Christmas" once. I suppose it's the retelling of the story that's the tradition!

Each year after our scrumptious buffet, we read the Christmas story. Following Wayne's reading, we share personal thoughts about the true meaning of Christmas, and Wayne leads us in a prayer, thanking God for sending His Son Jesus, Who is the true meaning of Christmas.

I'd like to say the spiritual mood lingers, but not so. We're too wound up. We quote "The Night Before Christmas" as best we can, stopping partway through when we remember we've left out something.

"Didn't we forget the part about the 'obstacles mount to the sky'?" someone will say, "and what about 'the leaves before the wild hurricane fall'?" We begin again, but never quite get it right.

Next we pile cookies on a plate for Santa (Christmas morning we find handwritten notes with such bizarre remarks as "Burp!" or "Your cookies made my reindeer sick!"). After everyone is finally in bed, Santa goes to work—making the family room look like a window in a department store, laying the wood for an early morning fire, and getting the big coffee pot ready to plug in.

By five-thirty the next morning, if Wayne can hold off that long, we're all wide-eyed and ready to see what Santa has brought.

It takes several hours to open gifts. We do it one-at-a-time and "ooh and ahhh" over each one. Clothes are modeled on the spot. Then the traditional breakfast—ham slabs cooked outside on the grill, steeplechase eggs, my chicken-liver stroganoff, Dana's cheese grits, and Becky's incredible zucchini bread. Later in the day, after naps, we have our Christmas dinner with all the trimmings.

Savoring all these wonderful memories made me realize I had no intention of walking off into the sunset to spend Christmas with Elvis! *But then again*, I thought, *this could be my last*. A lot can happen in a year.

What I really wanted to do was have a pity party, but instead I had a long talk with myself. *Snap out of it!* and *Stop your mullygrubbing!* didn't seem to be working too well. I reminded myself I'd been the center of attention for almost a year. Food had been planned to my liking and schedules arranged for my benefit. My family and friends had become my servants, and everything had revolved around me. Perhaps it was time to change that.

Maybe the reason was selfish—*If this truly is my last year, then I want my family to remember wonderful me!* Whatever my motive, I later realized it *was* a turning point. It would have been easy to stay where I was with people catering to my whims.

I've met several women who have never managed to get beyond this point. One woman told me, "I had cancer twenty-five years ago [she told me about it in *great detail*], and even though they tell me I'm cured, I just never got over it; my family still has to do everything for me."

After that I wrote a little sign and put it on the wall by my desk that said: "Dear God, please spare me from other women's cancer stories." Maybe I could at least *snap part of the way out of it* for the Christmas season—maybe mullygrub slightly less.

Something comes over you when you face the possibility of dying; not only do you feel a compulsion to get your house in order—throw away the ragged underwear and clean out the drawers—but there is an overwhelming need to leave something significant behind as a reminder of your life.

For the first time I wrote a Christmas letter, hoping my friends would tuck it away and save it. "Sue's last letter," they would say. I took care not to mention cancer or sickness. After all, I didn't want them say, "Sue's last letter was a real downer. Pitiful . . . just pitiful!" Instead I wrote:

Dear Friends:

As I write this, we're in windy, cold Chicago. Once again, Wayne has kept his promise (made fifteen years ago) that he'd bring me back to do my Christmas shopping and see the sights only a big city can offer.

The snow is blowing wildly, but we are snuggled into our hotel room for the night. What fun we've had eating in our favorite places, enjoying the beauty of North Michigan Avenue with its millions of tiny white lights . . . and shopping . . . special things for the girls gift-wrapped as only Saks can do. A black satin hat for me with a veil down to my chin! Wayne carried the packages and the shopping bags and didn't grumble, not even when I bought the hat . . . only when I wore it!

It's late now, and Wayne is sleeping, but my mind is full of things I want to do this Christmas season . . . fill the cookie jar, light the hill to our house with little white lights like Michigan Avenue, and invite everyone over, especially those I haven't seen for a long time.

My heart is overflowing with joy, and I'm so very grateful. First of all, for one of God's very best ideas . . . friends! Grateful too for my family! For Mindy, who fills my life with fun and little surprises like a love note tucked in my suitcase or flowers by my bed when I wake up. For Dana, who moved into her very own apartment just a couple of miles away but comes home several times a week because she's "homesick." And Wayne, who has given me more love and cherishing than I knew was possible in the almost twenty-five years since he promised to do that.

At this time when "peace on earth" is utmost in our minds, the profundity of Scripture rings forth for all time to those who believe: "Peace I leave with you; my peace I give you. . . . Do not let your hearts be troubled and do not be afraid."

Love,
Sue

The letter out of the way, I could concentrate on special gifts for my family. Never before had I thought so diligently about what to give. I knew my sympathetic family would understand if I gave them nothing. What a year it had been with the mastectomy, the diagnosis, the aggressive treatment, and Mother's illness and death.

While I was planning my last Christmas with my family, Wayne was going through his own dilemma. For years he'd admired a diamond ring guard that would encase my emerald-cut engagement ring and he secretly planned to buy it for me for our twenty-fifth wedding anniversary, a year and a half away. His problem was that I might not live that long. After much thought he decided I would have my ring guard for Christmas.

A week before, my daughter happened to notice I'd lost the emerald-cut diamond from my engagement ring. We searched the house over but it was nowhere to be found. "Like finding a needle in a haystack," I commented and reminded myself it was insured and it could be replaced. Wayne wasn't so easily placated. In fact, I'd never seen him so upset. "Honey, it's okay," I told him. "We can take care of it after Christmas, when things aren't so busy." He worried about it constantly and crawled around on his hands and knees peering under every piece of furniture in the house. I could see he was terribly upset, but didn't know the reason.

Four days before Christmas, I was sitting at the kitchen table with Mary Shillis, Mindy's best friend and our neighbor, when she jumped to her feet, ran to the corner where we feed the cats, moved their dish aside, and yelled, "I found it. Call Wayne!" Wayne was home in a matter of minutes, grabbed the stone and the ring, and breathlessly exclaimed, "Don't worry. I'll get it fixed for you!"

When I opened my package on Christmas morning there was my ring surrounded by fourteen sparkling diamonds. I was surprised and Wayne was glowing. Sure, he had some frantic moments, but ultimately his gift was presented in the very best possible way.

I often remind Wayne that by threatening to die, I tricked him into buying me the beautiful ring and then tricked him again by being alive for our twenty-fifth anniversary so he would have to buy another present!

The dilemma of what I could give my loved ones loomed. One day as I was straightening the laundry room the answer came when I picked up a ragged quilt that had been passed down through the family. As I unfolded it, a flood of memories unfolded with it, and an idea as well. *I'll frame several of the large designs and give them to my daughters and brothers; I'll write my memories of the quilting bee and the ladies who created this beautiful work of art.* I continued to play out the scene in my mind:

I can see it now. Someday when one of my daughters is famous, she'll be asked, "What was your best Christmas gift ever?" She'll think a moment and answer, "The last year my mother was with us she had some pieces from an old quilt framed . . ." Tears would come to her eyes and her voice would break; then she'd repeat the story attached to the back of the frame.

Well, it may not happen exactly as I've described it here, but on Christmas morning when I presented what I thought was to be my *final* gift to my daughters and brothers, there wasn't a dry eye as we read the story aloud together.

CHRISTMAS 1983

My gift to you is a sunflower . . . and a story

This pattern is called Sunflower, and this tattered piece was once part of a quilt made by the ladies of the

Langsville, Ohio, Christian Church, where my grandparents attended. My first memory of it is tracing its pattern as I lay on the daybed at Grandma Entsminger's. When my grandmother died, it was my mother's, and for years it was folded at the foot of her bed.

When it became mine, I had no idea of its value or the sentiments I should have felt. I took it on picnics, used it as a tablecloth, and spread it on the floor when I rolled around with my babies. I bleached it and put it through too many washings until it was worn and falling apart. Still I couldn't throw it away. The patterns were too beautiful. Maybe in this frame, its beauty will last another generation or two. Here's its story:

When I was a child, I used to spend weeks at a time with Grandpa and Grandma Entsminger at their home in the country near Langsville. Church was important to the community, and since there was only one, the Christian Church, that's where everyone went (Aunt Maggie always attended but reminded us she was really a Presbyterian since she continued to hold her membership in the Presbyterian church in Zanesville).

I was fascinated by the pump organ and even more so with Clarice, the lady who played it. Clarice had been Mother's friend since they were young girls. She was beautiful, though born crippled—in those days, they called it *hunchback*—and to me her predicament seemed both tragic and dramatic. I couldn't keep my eyes off her, and when I got home I would hurry to the piano and pretend that I too was hunchbacked!

The church didn't have a minister—at least not regularly—but it did have a choir. Visitors were invited to sing, and as soon our family walked in, we were ushered up the center aisle past the potbellied stove to the choir loft. Daddy would sing at the top of his voice; I would be more than a little embarrassed.

Quilting day, which was held in different homes, was a monthly occasion and the ladies arrived early, prepared to spend as many hours as possible. They would set up their quilting frame, drape their unfinished work across it, take their places around it, and begin a wonderful day of gossiping, laughing, and eating. As they stitched and chatted, their fingers were busy creating beautiful kaleidoscopes of colorful fabric bits that became a work of art. More importantly for them, a blanket of warmth to keep out the cold of a winter's night.

The busy scene, like a Norman Rockwell painting, is still in my mind; but most of all, I remember impressions of ordinary people creating a masterpiece.

Mrs. Laidley was rather heavy, but that wasn't important in those days. In fact I heard them say that a hefty woman was a good sign her husband was supporting her well. Laurie Folden, my grandma's best friend, was small and fragile looking. Her son was a pilot and once landed his plane in the pasture next to her house. They talked about that for years.

I remember Elsie, whose laughter was loud and boisterous, and I wonder now if her handiwork was a bit less exact than the others since she was having such a hilariously good time.

Aunt Annie's stitches were probably tight just like she held her needle . . . and her mouth even more so. I could tell from her voice she was often sad and worried about things the others never even thought of. I knew Aunt Annie's story, although she never spoke of it.

One morning her young husband had kissed her goodbye and gone outside and shot himself. They found his body by the fence. I never heard an explanation as to why, but in those days children didn't ask questions. No wonder, though, there wasn't as much joy in Aunt Annie's heart as there was in the hearts of her quilting sisters who had loving husbands to cook and bake and do for.

Aunt Maggie had an edge on the others. She'd been to California—her daughter lived there—and she knew firsthand what *they* were doing in California. She'd even taken ceramics while she was there and brought back samples of her handiwork. And of course, Aunt Maggie was a Presbyterian.

Barbara, the local beautician, didn't make it to quilting day. Maybe that was good because it gave the others a good chance to discuss the fact that she had divorced her husband and had bleached her hair to boot! Neither of those things had been done in Langsville before!

... and so, those country women and others who've faded from my mind worked together making a necessary household item. Little did they know as they pursued their routine, their ritual, that they were creating a treasure of history for us to enjoy. All that's left is a sunflower ... a piece of history ... and a story ...

... and that's my gift to you.

Celebrating Your Friends

It HAPPENS to some people in the spring; to others in the fall. It happens to me immediately after Christmas. Each year as I pack away the Christmas decorations, I am consumed by the need to get organized! Even though I had a knot in my stomach, a reminder that a treatment was just around the corner, this year was no different.

I carefully wrapped the glass cookie jars that sit on my kitchen cabinets during the holidays, the toys that line the stairway, the front-door arrangement, the manger scene, and the tree ornaments. *As long as I've gone this far, I may as well organize closets and shelves,* I thought. If I die before next Christmas, at least no one will have reason to say I was messy!

Beginning with the shelves in the garage, I threw away twinkly lights that hadn't lit up for years, much less twinkled. I tossed out rusted cookie tins that looked as if they'd been used in rowdy games of kick-the-can. Out went the pitiful papier-mâché angels that seemed more like street people than heavenly beings.

In the closet under the stairway, I discovered and got rid of nine duffel bags we hadn't used in years. In the family room I found three empty drawers—a direct gift from God—and in the guest room I discovered a treasure!

There we have an old French china cabinet that stands with its glass doors swung open to display our *junkories*, a cross between junk and memories. There are museum replicas that Wayne and I brought back from a trip to Greece years ago, interesting containers we chose from the Russian Pavilion gift shop at the Montreal World's Fair, old family pictures in their original cardboard frames, and an assortment of antiques.

From Wayne's side of the family, there's a beat-up wooden shoe form, a delicate fringed linen hand towel, and his father's baby shoes. From my side, there's a tiny gilded French mirror, a small cheese basket, a miniuadere evening purse, and two well-worn autograph books that had belonged to my grandparents, Lewis and Carrie Entsminger.

I reached for one of them and examined the beautifully tooled leatherwork. Slivers of aged, brownish paper flaked into my hands and floated to the carpet like a lazy snowfall. It was curious that this book had been in my possession for years and yet I'd never looked at it.

What words of wisdom might Grandma's friends have to offer, I wondered as I opened the book. I moved to sit on the bed and sank back into the pillows, noting the date on the first page. How ironic that a hundred years to the *exact* day had passed since that entry. A shiver went through me, as sometimes happens when such a strange coincidence takes place. It was as though it were preplanned, inevitable, that I would pick up *that* book on *that* day.

Grandma's friends had penned such lovely sentiments and I began to think about my own friends and acquaintances, especially those who had taken the time to write and send cards during my illness. It seemed as though the *right card*, with the *right sentiment*, always arrived at just the *right time*.

Donna and Murray sent a card every week for the entire year I was taking chemotherapy. Sometimes they were fat-little-cherub-and-cabbage-rose effusive, but more often than not, they were grab-your-stomach-and-bend-double funny! Laughter! Better than medicine in my opinion.

Some of Grandma's friends mentioned the silly things they'd done together and I couldn't help but think of all the crazy things

I'd done with my own friends. Regular old junior high school slumber parties, for instance! "Wayne's out of town," I'll say.

"So's Bob," Joy will answer, "let's have a slumber party." The group can include Gloria, Peggy, Joy, Evelyn, Marty, Lynn, Lisa, Linda, or Judy—whoever can make it. The more, the merrier!

I thought about our "girls only" vacations, which may seem strange to some people. To us it's a different kind of relaxation from trips with our husbands. It's worth it if only to be free from TV. Men turn it on when they walk in the room; women rarely do.

Another thing is food. You don't hand a man a Spam on white bread! Men want real meals and they want them *when* they want them.

"Have we made reservations?"

If the answer is yes, then it's, "Why so late?" or just as likely, "Why so early?"

"What kind of place is it? Is it good?"

"Well, gee, I don't know. It says here in the travel guide, it's *bad!* Last tourists who ate there died of ptomaine poisoning!"

And I won't get into the fact that women just kind of mosey off to bed when they feel so inclined, while men say, "Time to go to bed." If we ignore them, they'll say it a little louder: "Time to go to bed!" And if we still ignore them, they'll repeat it, adding, "I'm tired. Aren't *you* tired?"

Many times our women-only trips start out as husband trips and the men conk out on us; men have such a hard time coordinating their schedules. When we do manage to arrange a couples vacation, we love it. It can't be beat for fun and excitement, and we pack in enough fun and adventure to last a long time.

My mind wandered back to my grandparents. Except for the few stories that had made their way through the next generation, I knew very little about them. Would my stories bear repeating to my progenitors? Heaven knows our stories should be well preserved, as many times as we tell them. My friends and I *thrive* on our stories! We tell them over and over, and to us they become more interesting each time they are told because we've given each other permission to exaggerate. The flying roach that attacked Marty and me one night in Cayman has grown to man-eating proportions in the retelling. Peggy putting the wrong kind of soap in the dishwasher causing it to overflow, now sounds like the highlight of our vacation! Another memorable Cayman adventure was performing a song and dance routine from *Singin' in the Rain*, outdoors during a torrential nor'wester, complete with plastic garbage-bag costumes. In the retelling, the performance now equals an opening night on Broadway.

Do we want to hear once again about Lynn's old boyfriend? . . . my old boyfriend? . . . Joy's friend who became a breast doctor? Is there a *National Enquirer?*

Friendship, I believe, is built on history, and the telling and retelling of that history cements the friendship.

Before my mastectomy, year of chemotherapy, and reconstructive surgery, things like this didn't matter that much. Let's face it, I wasn't the world's most caring, nurturing, *do-unto-others, love-your-neighbor-as-yourself* kind of person—although I would feed someone's cat if asked.

For a while after my mastectomy and the resulting bad news, I preferred to *observe* life rather than *participate* in it. I watched people come and go; I saw them talk, laugh, and touch; and I simply wanted to watch. It was as though I wondered what life would be like without me.

Eventually, I moved through that stage and on to a level of participation I never before knew was possible. I didn't want to miss anything! In fact, the trips, the slumber parties, photo albums, and journals have been *since* my cancer surgery. Suddenly I had a new zest for living; and because friendship (with both men and women, and even with my own family) was such an integral part of living, I began evaluating what it meant to be a friend.

An important thing I learned was that people can do only what people can do! Had I realized this before, I would have spent less time being judgmental, asking, *Why didn't he do this?* or *Why didn't she do that?*

There were people who seemed glib in regard to my illness, ready with an easy answer. Others made me feel as though what I was going through was worse than it actually was. Some even treated me as though I were dying. That was difficult for me; however as time passed, I began to realize that each person sees things from his or her own personal perspective.

I've always loved to read biographies, especially about political figures. I'll read anything and everything about the Kennedys, short of the *National Enquirer* (and I'll do that in a supermarket line, if push comes to *push!*). When I see "Kennedy gives birth to two-headed baby" (perhaps that's one of the few things they haven't done!), I don't even look over my shoulder to see if the pastor is behind me; I just grab and read!

One of my favorite examples of personal perspective is from a Jackie Kennedy biography in which Lyndon Johnson was making an effort at friendship with Jackie after President Kennedy's death. He sent her flowers, invited her over, and even offered her positions in his administration.

On one occasion, he called her *sweetheart* and actually ordered her to *get on over to the White House and start living again*. She was so infuriated, both about being called *sweetheart* and about his condescending attitude, that she referred to him as "an over-sized cow-punching oaf"!

When told that Jackie was upset, Johnson answered, "Where I come from, we call the ladies *sweetheart*, and the ladies call their gentlemen *honey*. I've bent over backwards for that woman. I've done cartwheels and deep-knee squats, and all I get is criticism."

Lyndon Johnson was just Lyndon Johnson *being* Lyndon Johnson, with his own set of baggage that came from Texas roots; Jackie was being Jackie, whose feelings were conditioned by her refined progenitors. Each could be nothing less, nothing more.

In a time of life crisis, people are especially vulnerable to the seeming insensitivity of another person's perspective. An author, writing about her mother's illness, tells of a minister who drove six hundred miles to see her mother but didn't do what they'd expected—didn't offer the comfort they'd hoped for. Does the six-hundred-mile drive count for nothing?

If I had to reduce this chapter to only one thought, it would be to accept the deep-knee squats, and to gather up the gifts people offer one by one and put them in a big basket (figuratively speaking, of course). You'll find the gifts that are brought have a marvelous variety of intangible, immutable qualities, such as humor, joy, acceptance, good conversation, touching, crying, listening, surprise, prayer, and—perhaps the greatest gift of all—time. That basket, that source, will provide everything you need to get through an illness—or through life, for that matter! So reach in the basket and take what you need as you need it. Use it! Savor it! If there's anything left, PASS IT ON; but, for heaven's sake, don't expect everyone's gift to be the same.

Peggy kissed me on the lips during my illness (still does), and her gift to me was "acceptance." She didn't seem to be worried about catching the plague. Some people turned away from me or covered their mouths, not wanting to breathe my air.

Joy, who we tease about carrying Lysol in her purse to decontaminate toilet seats, could never kiss me, then or now! But Joy knows how to celebrate! She could celebrate a dead dog! She gave me the gift of "celebration" at every step of the mastectomy, chemotherapy, and reconstructive surgery.

"Another thing behind us," Joy would say as she came up with a new way to celebrate—a box lunch at the office with animal crackers for dessert; a children's book she would read aloud to me with all the sound effects (much as you would read to a child); parties of all varieties; and the grand finale, a trip to the Grand Cayman Islands.

Joe Shillis, our neighbor, wouldn't think to plan a trip to an exotic island, and Joe doesn't know how to plan parties. He would probably think some of Joy's shenanigans to be downright silly; but he knows how to do other things that lift the spirit. He knows whether the funny noise my car is making is serious or not, if I should cover my plants because of frost, whether there is too much wind to fish, and knows how to cry with me. How rare in a man!

Joe came to the hospital, took my hands in his rough ones, and looked into my eyes, and our tears poured. Alice, Joe's wife, was my first visitor each day, having made a stop at church to light a candle signifying her prayers for me.

I didn't know Locher very well at all, so it was a complete surprise when he visited me in the hospital. From my bed I could see a tall, lanky figure pacing back and forth in the hall as though undecided about coming in. It took me a moment to recognize this well-dressed man in a three-piece gray suit. Before I'd only seen him in his white work shirt that said "Locher Bibb" on his left pocket, just beneath "J. B. Cook Auto Parts."

I motioned him in; after a brief greeting, Locher sat down close to me, put his head in his hands, and said, "My first wife died of that!" I was taken aback to say the least, but when I looked in his eyes, I knew that what he was really saying was, "I understand."

Many of my male friends were uncomfortable with the fact I'd lost a breast. They were uncomfortable with the "B" word, and they would look at the ceiling, with an occasional hope-I-don't-get-caught glance "you know where."

I had two friends—Chris, a young businessman, and Michael, an artist who visited me almost every day. They thought nothing of climbing up on the bed with me, as though it were a slumber party.

"With those legs, who needs breasts?" was one of Chris's lines. I can't repeat Michael's comment when he arrived with a dozen balloons!

There are those who would criticize the ribald humor of my guests, but the bantering and teasing made up one of my best gifts. It did a great deal for my self-esteem and my ability to think of myself as a normal woman.

Some friends didn't come to visit me in the hospital, but later showed up at my house with a casserole. The gift of "casserole" is one of the most important! Sometimes I threaten to get sick just to get some of Kate's lasagna, Alice's potato salad, or Evelyn's soup. Our church members do a remarkable job of caring for families in crises. They're good at feeding both body and soul.

During my illness, I discovered another whole circle of friends I didn't know existed, every-day-of-the-week people. Before, I was too busy for small talk and I was missing a whole chunk of life that I now hold dear. These every-day-of-the-week people are the folk who pass through my life coincidentally just because we are in the same place at the same time. As these people saw my vulnerability during the year I was in treatment, they questioned me with concern. Many asked if there was anything they could do. Some told me of their prayers for me.

I could easily have gone the rest of my life having lunch at Arnold's Country Kitchen, without saying much more than the words, "Meatloaf, mashed potatoes, fried apples, and greens." Jack Arnold could just as easily have filled my plate, pushed his cash register buttons, and taken my money. Now we make it an event.

"Sue Buchanan's here," he'll announce to everybody in the restaurant. Everybody can include country singers, advertising agency people, a former governor, and bums right off the street. "I gotta joke for you." He will dish out his joke as he dishes out his macaroni and cheese.

"What, no seats?" I say at the top of my lungs and laugh as I go through the line. "Throw somebody out; I need a table!" One of my proudest moments was when Jack featured my photography exhibit on the slightly greasy, plastic paneled walls of his down-home eating establishment. If I had a choice of showing off my work at Arnold's Country Kitchen or the National Gallery, it would be Arnold's in a New York minute.

I could go to Dillard's department store, buy my stockings and eyebrow pencil, check out the shoes, and get home twice as fast if I didn't stop to talk to Gloria. She has been selling me Shalimar since it was eight dollars a bottle. She cared that I was sick, and to this day, she never fails to ask whether I'm still okay.

"How are those little boogers doing?" the woman at the discount bread store asked me the other day.

"They were there the other night at five-fifteen, before it was even dark. Can you believe that? And the one we called Ricky is now Rhonda, because she had three babies," I explain as I pay for my day-old bread and hurry home to feed my not-so-wild raccoons.

The people at the drugstore—Mrs. Wolf, Ruth, and Dr. Stevens—expect me to stop by to say hello even when I have no prescriptions to fill. When Mrs. Wolf had breast cancer, I visited her at home because she wanted me to come. The gifts in my basket come not only from my close personal friends and acquaintances, but also from my every-day-of-the week friends. Often one of these people says the exact word of encouragement I need for the day.

The basket philosophy of friendship gives me incredible resources, but that's only half of the story. The other half is that I now have the responsibility and privilege of filling baskets myself; it is by far one of the most rewarding life experiences I have ever known—even when I'm sick and don't feel like it!

If It's Broken, Fix It!

That night in the hospital when the plastic surgeon told me about reconstructive surgery, I knew immediately I would choose that course of action, assuming of course, I had to have a mastectomy.

Even though I knew nothing about reconstructive breast surgery, I certainly wasn't ignorant about *plastic surgery*. I knew about it almost firsthand! This may sound like gossip, and I can't mention names, but some of my best friends have had it. There's rhinoplasty (care to guess the derivation of that word?) to correct noses that aren't just right, there's blepharoplasty for eyes that are puffy and have lost their lid definition, and there's liposuction to slurp away those little blobs of fat that make your clothes fit funny.

Occasionally whole faces must be lifted! My husband has observed that a certain country music star has had her face lifted so many times she doesn't have to bend over to pull up her socks—she simply raises her eyebrows! When certain things drop they must be propped! Need I say more?

Almost everyone I know who has had plastic surgery talks about it openly. Not everyone likes to make jokes about it. I learned that the hard way. My actions, I would like to point out, were egged on by my friends. It seems they would have counseled me to be more tactful. But even if they had, I probably would have done what I did anyway. Maybe I should have listened to Wayne, who pointed out that if you have to check with other people, then you probably shouldn't do it.

It happened this way. A young business associate of mine, who will go unnamed, didn't try to keep her plans for plastic surgery a secret; rather, she kept us posted each step of the way. She called it by its correct name, *rhinoplasty*; we called it a "nose job." She told us that she had been shown pictures of various nose structures, and with her doctor's help, she'd chosen the one that was best suited for her face. She explained there were claustrophobic aftereffects that would probably cause her to feel panicked and disoriented for a few days, but that she had thought of a way to counter them. She would pack her nose *before* the surgery and get used to it *ahead of time*. Such discipline!

The operation went as scheduled and I wracked my brain to think of some clever way to cheer her up, to help her celebrate her new nose. After all, that's what our group of friends does when one of us is in the hospital.

Bob still has the antique bedpan full of cactus we brought him ten years ago when he had his heart attack; if I live to be a hundred, I'll never forget the seafood buffet with all the trimmings Dan and Phyllis had delivered to my hospital room the night before my reconstructive surgery, or the cake Joy and Minnie brought. It was made to look like the torso—neck to thigh—of a large-breasted woman in a bikini. Every nurse, doctor, and ambulatory patient on the floor, as well as my dignified Presbyterian pastor, ended up in my room for a piece of cake before the evening was over.

My idea for cheering up my friend who was having rhinoplasty wasn't *that* bold, but seemed like a good idea. First of all, I baked a cake—a scratch cake. In retrospect, I can see that I should have simply delivered the cake, expressed my good wishes, and left. It was the homemade get well card that caused the problem.

"Choose which nose you would prefer." I printed in bold letters on the front.

"A funny one?" it said on page two where I pasted a picture of Mickey Mouse.

"A famous one?" it said beside Jacqueline Kennedy's photo.

"A political one?" beside the president's mug.

There were other pictures and other blurbs, but you get the idea! The punch line, I'm sure you've already guessed (now there's a commercial card like this—they stole my idea!): "Now that you've picked your nose, wash your hands and have some cake." I signed my name and set out to deliver the cake, chuckling all the way.

By the time I handed over my prize, I was smiling my toothiest smile. I couldn't wait for my friend to read the card. I waited for a reaction. I'm still waiting. She apparently saw no humor in it, no humor at all. I wasn't invited to stay for tea. I wasn't thanked. I didn't see her for days. When I did, she was cool and didn't mention my card. To this day, every time I see her beautiful profile, I wonder how I could have missed so completely.

So the card was tasteless. Sometimes *life* is tasteless!

Ah yes, "there is some myth for every man [and woman] if we but knew, it would make us understand all that he [she] did and thought." I didn't say that; Yeats did. However, I've pondered the concept more than once.

I don't know why one woman would choose plastic surgery and another wouldn't anymore than I know why years ago, when we lived on Sixth Street, our neighbor Simon Jones had such a fit when I cut his daughter Simona's never-been-touched-by-scissors hair. Even then aesthetics were important to me, and I knew at that tender age, Simona's haircut made her look 100 percent better! I thought the whole neighborhood would thank me.

When my mother hung up the phone, she asked in her most incredulous tone of voice: "Sue, did you cut Simona's hair?"

Before I could answer—and certainly before thinking to thank me—she turned to my father and said: "That was Simon Jones. Sue cut Simona's hair, and Simon is hoppin' mad!"

Now that I think of it, no one ever *did* thank me! That's twice!

Even as a child I was apparently vain. When I was three, I was in a fashion show at the People's Store. I did just as I was told until I got to the end of the runway. There I remained despite backstage whispers that grew louder and louder: "Pst! Sue, come back now ... Sue ... Sue ... *Suzanne!*"

Loving the attention, I kept parading around, adding bows and spins that weren't rehearsed until an embarrassed fashion director came to pull me out of the spotlight—but not before I caught sight of our neighbor, held the back of my skirt high above my head, gave a three-hundred-and-sixty-degree spin that revealed my underwear, and yelled, "Oh, Clurey (short for Mrs. McClure), isn't this the pwettiest dwess you ever laid eyes on?"

Not long after, of course, I became Mrs. Vandertweezers, dressed in my high-heeled shoes, a hat out to there, and the satin blouse that came down to my ankles. Under the satin blouse (did I mention?) were pinned my daddy's rolled-up socks for bosoms.

Mrs. Vandertweezers grew up to love flashy clothes right down to her underwear. Even there she much preferred leopard skin over plain cotton, trimmed in little animal parts if possible! An exaggeration of course, but the truth is Mrs. Vandertweezers still lived inside me; the lady had no intentions of filling her bra with rolled-up socks for the rest of her life! Reconstructive surgery was the only way to go.

Not long ago, I asked my plastic surgeon for my medical file to jog my memory as to the specifics of my reconstructive surgery. The first thing I noticed when I opened the file was a letter I'd written the week of my biopsy. It said, in part:

> You were the only ray of hope in a week filled with bad news. Thank you for being there.
>
> In the past two or three weeks it amazes me how many women have shared with me that they have had my same experience! It blows my mind that many women still don't know their options—especially that she doesn't have to live her life deformed.
>
> Thank you for loaning me the book. Hold a place for me in your busy schedule for a year from now—February or March—and then watch out! I have a lot of living to do!

The next thing that captured my attention was twenty-two pages of information about the doctor. I had asked his receptionist to include his bio when she sent my file. As I thumbed through his impressive list of accomplishments, it occurred to me that this was a first. I'd never been given—nor had I thought to ask for—this kind of information before. *It wouldn't be such a bad idea to put this on the list of things to ask for when doctor shopping*, I thought.

There was correspondence from Cowboy Doctor along with my records and pathology reports for both surgeries. His preoperative notes for the lumpectomy were easy to decipher.

> I first examined this 45-year-old white female on 1/14/83 as a referral from Dr. Tipton. The patient complained of a mass deep in the left breast which she had detected herself. She was particularly concerned because her mother had had carcinoma of the breast and she had recently had a friend die of carcinoma of the breast. On examination, the patient was found to have huge symmetrical breasts. At the 6 o'clock position half way between the central portion of the breast and its periphery deep in the breast, was a somewhat movable, well delineated, slightly irregular, 2 cm. mass. No axillary nodes were palpable. No other dominant masses were felt. In the office, I attempted to decompress the lesion by aspiration. The lesion could not be decompressed. Subsequently, a mammogram was obtained. The mammogram suggested that the lesion was likely malignant. Biopsy was advised. The patient requested that no procedure other than biopsy be carried out. She had not been able to bring herself to accept a mastectomy. The patient was thus admitted to the hospital for excisional biopsy.

Did I detect a note of sarcasm in those words? "The patient couldn't *bring* herself to accept a mastectomy." Not true! The patient suddenly realized she had options.

The pathology report was scary:

> The approximate center of the specimen has an unencapsulated, circumscribed, fleshy, gray nodule, measuring 1.6

cm. in diameter. Frozen section diagnosis is infiltrating duct carcinoma ... control is submitted in cassette FS–1 and representative selected sections are submitted in cassettes A, B and C. Tumor cells have large moderately plemorphic vesicular nuclei with prominent nucleoli and vacuolated cytoplasm.

That's just a portion of it and only for the lumpectomy. The report on the mastectomy is too frightening for words!

The next piece of correspondence is to my oncologist from my plastic surgeon. It speaks of my "guarded prognosis" and says that after discussing the various techniques of breast reconstruction, I "tentatively selected to undergo transverse rectus abdominus myocutaneous flap reconstruction of the left breast with the combined abdominal reconstruction (lipectomy)." That meant he would be making my new breast out of my stomach fat, but of course he couldn't afford to say it so simply. After all he had twenty-two pages of credentials!

The letter also discussed whether or not it would be a good idea at the time of reconstruction to remove the right breast due to the high probability of cancer recurring there. There are no further notes on this, but I remember that my oncologist recommended this precaution. The final paragraph says, "I wish her prognosis were better, as she certainly could give a ray of hope to many women who have breast cancer."

I remembered the fears. I also remembered the excitement when I knew at last that reconstructive surgery would be a reality. Finally I would be having my body fixed. For a year, I'd avoided undressing in front of my husband, chosen dresses with high necklines, and stayed clear of mirrors.

Getting up in the night to go to the bathroom was a nightmare in itself. Without my prosthesis my balance was off, and I would fall flat or at best stumble into the furniture. I was one big bruise waiting to happen. When I was dressed and had the weighty prosthesis in place, I was once again in balance.

I cringed at the thought of wearing a bathing suit. Before Wayne and I went to Puerto Rico, I bought one designed specifically for mastectomy patients. It had a high neckline but not high enough. When it was wet it drooped, and I was always pulling at it for fear it would reveal my concave chest. When I went for a dip, I would lay a coverup by the side of the pool so I could quickly put it on the minute I came up out of the water.

The other time I got an overdose of the hated bathing suit was when Joy took me to the Grand Cayman Islands as a reward for making it to the end of chemo and still being alive. There we wore our swimsuits all day every day, only dressing at night for dinner.

Knowing I'd be having reconstructive surgery as soon as I got back to Nashville helped, as every day I put on the bag-lady-baggy, dingy suit and self-consciously began my day. The first thing I was going to do when I got my body back was burn the ugly bathing suit. Then I'd buy a new one—a *pink* one!

When I realized I would like to write about reconstructive surgery and couldn't remember the details, my friend Rose Miller, who is a consultant to plastic surgeons, suggested I watch a surgery being performed. I loved the idea, and before I knew it, she had arranged it. I'd be observing a double mastectomy and reconstructive surgery that would use the patient's stomach tissue to form both new breasts. The woman didn't have cancer, but was plagued with suspicious lumps and a family history that put her at high risk. She was one of many women choosing prophylactic mastectomy as breast cancer prevention.

The day of surgery finally arrived; after I'd donned my scrubs, complete with hat, footies, and mask, I was invited to meet the patient. She was "happy" with medication and greeted me cheerfully and introduced me to her husband. Our mutual doctor explained to her why I was there—that I had experienced similar surgery and was writing a book to help other women. We had immediate rapport—in her drugged state she'd have had rapport with a chimpanzee!

"I saw your picture and note in the doctor's book," she chuckled. I knew she was referring to the snapshot of me in my pink bathing suit along with the note that said, "Thanks to you, women with remarkable bodies are sleazing the beaches of the world."

We chatted until the gurney pushers came to take her the short distance to the operating room.

As I walked out, her husband took her in his arms for a last embrace against what I observed as lush, full breasts. I wondered if they'd made love the night before and if she had sobbed silently in the night as I'd done before my mastectomy. I remembered my own doubts and my wondering if the same intimacy could ever again be achieved.

I walked through the doors with all the warning signs—the I-don't-want-to-know-what-goes-on-beyond-there double doors. I'd been in operating rooms dozens of times before for filming purposes. Usually one of the nurses volunteered to be the "patient," and we simulated the scene for benefit of the camera.

I glanced at the digital clock on the wall: 7:30.31. *Today it's for real*, I thought as I seated myself on a stool against the wall six or seven feet from the operating table. *I'll get used to it gradually; and as I do, I can move closer.* It occurred to me I didn't want to embarrass myself by passing out at the sight of blood.

Not too surprisingly, the thing that bothered me most was the odors: floor cleaner, antiseptic, bandages, iodine—the many things that combine to make up the hospital smell. It was overwhelming, and I wondered if I would last through the preliminaries.

I've always been affected by smells, whether it's floor cleaner, dry cleaning fluid, gasoline, or the scent wafting through Marshall Field's dressing room from the lady with the stinky armpits who was there before me. Even the room spray they use to cover the smells gags me. Blended together it becomes Stinky Lady Lemon, or Your Grandfather's Feet Eucalyptus. My "smell phobia" only got worse with chemotherapy and continues to this day.

It didn't take long to forget myself and be drawn into what was happening in the room. Like the players on a basketball team, the five members of this surgical team prepared for the "game." For the next five hours I watched them move as one well-oiled machine to accomplish one of the most incredible feats I've ever witnessed.

"Ready for some music?" one of the blue-clad women asked as she pushed a cassette into a player. Windham Hill-type music began to play. The patient chatted easily with the anesthesiologist. As the drugs dripped, dripped, dripped through the IV and into her arm, her words slowed until they were garbled, then incoherent, and finally nonexisting.

I remember the feeling well. For me it was as though I was traveling down a long tunnel, like the inside of a giant Slinky, toward the darkness of another planet.

How can anyone sleep in that light? The operating room was so bright it seemed to me like an overexposure, with light reflecting harshly off of the many stainless steel surfaces. Four giant octopus-like fixtures overhead could be moved back and forth to shine even more light on the working area. There must have been two hundred instruments: scissors, scalpels, needles of every size and shape, plus wicked-looking implements I couldn't identify.

The surgical staff wore unfashionable garb of green and blue that covered them from head to toe. Only their eyes were visible between mask and cap. No words were spoken. No time was wasted. Everyone had tasks to perform as the patient was readied for surgery.

The patient's head and outstretched arms were covered with green sheets; tight elastic stockings were pulled over her feet and onto her legs. They gave her shots, perhaps filled with a Novocaine-like substance, in her abdomen, her stomach, her breasts. Her body became a rag doll, not feeling a thing. Buttons were pushed on the operating table to reposition her body almost to a sitting position and pictures were taken. The time on the digital wall clock said 7:54.01.

On her body, the doctor mapped his plan with a big black felt marker. He drew generous, misshapen *lips* beginning above the navel and extending to the pubic hairline. Everyone relaxed as though they understood there was no damage done if the pen slipped. He continued his markings, but he was between me and the patient and was blocking my view.

"Hattie is having surgery next week. I can't imagine having you guys operate on me," said the male assistant. "If I've ever offended anybody in this room, I want you to know I'm sorry! I'd

hate to think you were mad at me when you cut me open." Everyone laughed.

The doctor stepped back and put the lid on his marker. Automatically three members of the team began swabbing the patient
with great quantities of iodine. The smell was strong. They chatted about ordinary things: a Christmas party, a new baby, and
midlife crises.

"Mine is almost over. I'm just about out of my Harley-David-
son stage." I couldn't tell if the anesthesiologist was actually into
motorcycles, or if the statement was for my benefit. He had a
twinkle in his eyes—eyes that quickly glanced in my direction and
back again to the panel of lights and gauges before him. Suddenly
everyone was aware of my presence. The doctor bent to allow one
of the nurses to place a steel halo on his head that held an intense
direct light.

"She's my circulator," he said, gesturing to the nurse. "She
anticipates my needs throughout the surgery. Problem is, when I
get home at night I don't have a circulator! My wife refuses!" We
laughed.

"Ask questions. Move closer. Feel free to walk around. We'll
tell you if you get in our way." I *would* have walked around if they
hadn't been about to cut. I lay my pad and pencil in my lap and
hung onto my seat with both hands.

It became quiet as incisions were made, first the abdomen and
then the breasts. I watched as the black lines became oozy with
blood as the scalpel followed the drawn patterns. I was surprised.
It was not all that gruesome. I leaned forward to get a better look.
Once again each person had a set of chores, all moving together,
communicating with a word or a gesture, sometimes with a look.
The doctor's sure hands worked quickly and expertly, occasionally signaling for an adjustment of the light on his brow or to the
operating table.

8:23.12—A breast was placed into a blue napkin. I didn't
remember getting up, but I was standing. Windham Hill had been
replaced by soft jazz.

8:50.22—Breast number two went into a blue napkin and I watched the surgical assistant trim slivers from it just as he had the other one. The two specimens were marked and handed out the door.

"To pathology," he explained for my benefit.

"The nipples," he said. I watched as, one at a time he balanced them on his index finger and trimmed away the excess flesh with a scissor-like instrument. He folded each one into a damp cloth and set it aside.

They do this almost every day, I thought. For me it was a once-in-a-lifetime experience.

Once again the mood relaxed a moment as the surgeon stretched his arms and shoulders. He explained that samples from each breast were sent to pathology, and that if there was no malignancy, they would sew the nipples back on. If cancer was present, they would make new nipples, using pieces of skin from the very tops of the insides of the thighs and grafting them to the proper place. This would form the areola. The nipple itself was simply a trick of the trade. With a few extra stitches a sack or protrubance is made—a fake nipple.

I remembered that procedures such as these are outlined in medical textbooks just as sentence diagrams are outlined in English books, but I was no less impressed!

Sometimes I couldn't tell whose hands were whose. They worked together like a big surgical octopus with a single mind—thinking, willing, judging, perceiving, and implementing. While the doctor, with the help of his assistant, was working to remove the breasts, two others were trimming skin from stomach tissue and tying off veins. They traded places as the doctor stepped in to accomplish another task.

A bluesy Memphis song was playing ... and my goodness! I was practically hanging over their shoulders!

"Tell me if I get in your way," I said as I circled the room to watch from a different perspective.

I moved to stand by the anesthesiologist and watch a small accordion in a jar. The tune it played was *beep, beep, beep.* There were two cylinders that appeared to be filled with oatmeal. Probably not.

His gaze intent on his gauges and note-taking, this *doctor of sleep* missed nothing. His big brown eyes—all that showed between mask and cap—were as interesting as the apparatus he was so carefully monitoring.

"This is a pulse oximeter ... measures the saturation of oxygen in the blood ... new in the last six or seven years ... life saver ... catastrophic possibilities before!" He explained his bailiwick to me in unfinished sentences, his attention never straying from the dials and gauges. I looked over his shoulder and saw the perfectly written notes on the chart.

I could only think of dumb questions like why the patient has to take off her fingernail polish prior to surgery. I'd been told it's because the anesthesiologist looks at your nails to determine whether you are getting enough oxygen, but he hadn't looked at her sheet-encased fingers once! Wouldn't it be funny if the new oximeter made the check-the-fingernail method obsolete and they had forgotten to tell Big Nurse Battle-ax?

Having made a complete circle around the room, I stopped at the foot of the table. What a dramatic view! It was like looking into a cavern. Even though the patient's torso was wide open, I was not one bit grossed out. In fact, I saw that a tunnel was being forged and I was enthralled at the beauty of the inside of the human body. A verse of Scripture popped into my mind: "I praise you because I am fearfully and wonderfully made; your works are wonderful" (Psalm 139:14).

Colorfully made too! There must have been twenty shades of red, from vivid coral to the palest pink and every hue in between. The bright color of blood, I expected. What I didn't expect were reds as varied as a lipstick display. And who would have thought there'd be yellow ... an abundance of yellow and the creamiest cream I could ever have imagined. These weren't innards; this was art! If I could capture the scene inside that cavity on canvas, it could hang in the Museum of Modern Art.

I pondered the Scripture again; suddenly I wanted to shout it out, but the timing wasn't right, to say the least! It was quiet again but for the private language of the operating room. They seemed to understand one another; however, to me it sounded like a tribal language.

Ush shoon n tupa unna umphaz. Barely a whisper but the circulator hurried to adjust the doctor's headlight once again. The air was thick with serious business. I watched amazed as hunks of stomach were tunneled through the passageway, bringing with them a blood supply vital to the success of the journey.

"Sue, look at this." I bent over the doctor's shoulder to see him pull flaps of skin over each mound of tissue. Voila! It looked like breasts to me. The clock read 10:46.24.

"Nose itchin' like crazy." This time I understood the words. He was gesturing frantically, his gooey latex-gloved hands in the air. His surgical nurse, also with gooey latex-gloved hands, rushed to his side. He rubbed his nose hard against her shoulder. "Ah, better!" The tension was broken for a moment; then once again they concentrated on their work; not a word or a motion was wasted.

By now I had noticed a pattern. Total silence was in order when they cut, and minimal chatter was permitted when they stitched. Once in a while, between tasks, there was a semblance of actual conversation and an occasional joke. They continued their stitching and they braced their elbows wherever they could to get the best angle—against rib cage, thigh, shoulder—wherever.

Ah-ha! I thought as I remembered the many unexplainable sore spots in my body after reconstructive surgery.

The phone rang and the receiver was held to the doctor's ear.

"Frozen section's benign," he said to no one in particular. "Go tell her husband there's no cancer. Tell him we're almost finished and I'll be up to talk to him when I'm done. Let's have some Christmas music." The mood became festive.

Like Santa's elves they stitched—two working on the stomach area, the doctor and his assistant hard at work on the breasts.

Someone was whistling softly behind his mask. They used circular needles, shaped like a big "C," just like the ones I used in hat-making class years ago. I never got the hang of it. I couldn't imagine it in latex gloves.

The nipples were removed from their safekeeping in the damp napkins and placed in their proper position. The surgeon's agile fingers formed the tiny stitches . . . so perfect, so uniform. It seemed to take forever. My body was tense, as though the responsibility for the outcome was on my shoulders alone. The last stitch was finally taken and the operating table was positioned to put the patient in a semi-sitting position. Everyone moved to the foot of the table. I was motioned along. We admired our accomplishments. Someone took a picture.

"Perfect! Good job. Nice work." Everyone was congratulating each other. I held myself back. It was probably not appropriate to cheer. I thanked everyone over and over as I pulled off my scrubs. I was supposed to take a break, call the office, and return phone calls, but I had been so captivated I forgot.

I made it to the parking garage before the impact of it all hit me. I stepped into the elevator with four other people and was about to confide what a rough morning I'd had due to the extraordinary surgery "we" just performed, when the man nearest the controls turned to me expectantly.

"Floor?" he questioned. I didn't have the slightest idea where I had parked my car or if I even had a car. My mind was blank. Finally, I recovered enough to blurt out a number and then tried to appear nonchalant as each time the door opened, I looked desperately for my car. I went all the way to the roof and back, getting off on each floor. Finally I remembered I was parked in the basement. By the time I reached my car my legs had turned to jelly. I fumbled with the lock and managed to get myself inside; immediately I broke out in a cold sweat.

I survived the knife, the sight of blood, and the rest, I thought; *now I'm going to pass out.*

I must have sat in my car for twenty minutes before I started the motor. I was overwhelmed to think that the surgery on my own body had been almost identical to what I had just watched. The only difference was the diagnosis; mine was cancerous. I thought of the responsibility borne by the doctor, his assistants, and the hospital. I remembered my surgeon, the one I'd made fun of so often. He was dead—dead of AIDS because he took on the responsibility of treating patients no one else wanted anything to do with.

It never occurred to me until that day what it might be like to be accountable to a patient, to a patient's family, to the community, and to God for a human life.

The next day I went by to visit the patient. She was propped up in bed and surrounded by family. We chatted as though we were old friends.

"I can't wait to see 'em." She pointed to her bandaged chest. "The first thing I'm going to do when these bandages come off is buy a bathing suit."

I could understand that. After all, that's exactly what I did—buy a bathing suit. I'll never forget the circumstances surrounding or following the first time I wore it.

I was self-conscious when I sunned by the pool at the magnificent Anatole Hotel in Dallas. *Should I even be wearing a bathing suit?* I wondered. Afterward I bathed, dressed, and took the elevator down to the hotel lobby. I felt wonderful! I felt like a new person. I *was* a new person. I threw my shoulders back at the thought of my newly constructed body. With my clothes on, I knew I looked better than I'd looked before. I had beautiful new breasts and a flat tummy.

As I walked across the elegant oriental carpets, I stopped to talk to friends. These were more than business acquaintances; these were folks we'd worked with for years. We produced their annual meetings, doing multi-image extravaganzas, video, speech writing, and being part of the team that gave birth to concepts that would propel this Fortune 500 company through another year.

"Join us," my friends invited. As I took my seat, a very nice-looking man, perhaps ten years my junior, turned to me and introduced himself. "We haven't met, but I saw you at the pool this afternoon in that pink bathing suit. You looked so pretty." I glanced at Kate who knew my story. She winked.

There are those who might say the Lord wouldn't hear the grateful prayer of a vain woman who has just had a strange man make a personal remark in a hotel lounge. Perhaps not, but I did utter a silent prayer of thanksgiving: *Thank You, God, for this affirmation. You know how much I needed it. The plastic surgeon might have remade me, but I know who did the original construction work, right down to the blueprints. Amen.*

Having new breasts is better than having a new dress or new draperies. I found myself showing them off to any female friend who appeared to be interested. One friend was out of town when I had my reconstructive surgery. The minute she got home she dialed my number.

"How do they look? I can't wait to see. What are you doing right now? I'll be right over."

I finally managed to get a word in to say that Wayne was out of town and I was starved and why didn't we meet at Dalt's for a bite to eat.

"Then we can run over to your house and I can see your new body," she replied.

Fifteen minutes later when I arrived at the restaurant, she was already seated and grinning from ear to ear. Before I could scoot into my side of the booth, she was on her feet and hopping around like a Pooh bear, leading the way to the ladies' room and straight into one of the miniature stalls.

She pulled my purse from my shoulder onto her own, put her hands on her hips, and waited with anticipation as I unbuttoned my shirt and pulled it open with a flourish.

"Ta-da!" I said as I threw out my underwear-*less* chest. "Wha'da ya think?"

"They are beautiful. Just beautiful!" she exclaimed.

"Feel them. They feel so natural," I encouraged. She reached out, poking here and there, oohing and ahhing over my new breasts.

"They feel natural just like mine," she said.

A few years before, I'd sat by her bedside after breast surgery, not because she had had a mastectomy, but because she was flat as a pancake and wanted breasts. Not bigger breasts, just breasts! It wasn't a secret; I'd seen her breasts before and after, so what happened next seemed quite natural.

"Feel mine," she said as she pulled up her shirt.

"You're right. They do feel the same," I agreed. "They really feel natural."

"We're sure fortunate, aren't we?" We adjusted our bodices and were shaking our heads at the wonder of it all as we opened the door of the stall and walked into five—count 'em—teeny-boppers standing in a line, eyes wide, mouths gaping. They had obviously heard every word we had said; we were everything their mothers had warned them about!

Show me a woman with implants and I'll show you an exhibitionist. Modest women become brazen when it comes to new breasts, and it's not at all unusual for a group of grown women to play "I'll show you mine, if you show me yours" simply because we never quite get over the wonder of it all.

I've never had a problem with my implants, and I've come to the happy conclusion that women with implants aren't dropping like flies as the media would have us believe. In the almost fifteen years since my surgery I've talked to hundreds of women who have them; I only know of two or three who have had honest-to-goodness problems.

My friend Patty woke up one morning, looked in the mirror, and realized one of her saline implants had gone flat. She called her doctor, scheduled day surgery to have it replaced. That was that. In her words, "I had a flat tire and I got it fixed."

Another person I know who had problems had a doctor who had never before performed the procedure. Not only wasn't he board certified, he wasn't even a plastic surgeon!

It seems to me implants should be available for mastectomy patients and for those who simply want bigger breasts. It should be a woman's choice.

The federal government has other ideas. They've decided women need to be protected from implants, even though only a small percentage have problems. If the government would be consistent, maybe I could understand. For instance, there is an *absolute* cause and effect between alcohol and tobacco and the death rate; yet the FDA doesn't pull liquor and cigarettes off the market. It certainly doesn't ask users to sign releases and fill out forms so they can keep track of them, which a person has to do to get implants. I believe the patient should be educated to the risks and should be tracked, but I think the choice should be voluntary.

Continual scares by the media and the unreasonable FDA controls have caused manufacturers to pull out of the market, thus slowing research and development to a snail's pace. Insurance carriers, eager for disclaimers, are rethinking coverage, and greedy lawyers have pushed patients into litigation. Women who have begun the reconstructive surgery process are often in limbo, second-guessing their own decisions and those of their doctors. The tragedy may be that the next generation (my own daughters included) will avoid self-examination and mammograms because reconstructive surgery is such an enigma.

My advice to a woman who is in a quandary about implants is to find an experienced, board-certified plastic surgeon, talk through the options and risks, then make an informed decision. While you are there, learn about other procedures that might be of interest. There are many women who wouldn't even entertain the thought, but my observation is that the positives of a good self-image outweigh the potential problems.

Milestones — A Vacation, a Party, and a Wedding

It was a perfect gift from a perfect friend. "Make it through the year of chemo, behave yourself, stay alive, and I'll take you to Grand Cayman," Joy promised. As the trip was planned and the time drew near, I wondered what kind of company I would be. I felt worn down, to say the least, and somewhat out of touch with reality. It was still as though life was happening in another dimension just out of my reach. I could see it and hear it but not quite be a part of it.

No sooner had we arrived at our condominium than Joy asked if I'd like to learn to snorkel. "Yeah . . . er . . . uh, sure . . . sounds fun," I answered haltingly, not wanting to disappoint her. She didn't seem to notice how unenthusiastic I was.

"First thing in the morning," she said like a first-grade teacher.

The next morning I had my first and only snorkel lesson—in the swimming pool. Either I was a fast learner or Joy was a good teacher; perhaps both. I was good! I was ready to spend the day snorkeling—in the swimming pool! Joy had other ideas.

"See that dark area out there?" she asked, pointing out to sea. "Think you can swim that far? That's a reef and the snorkeling there is great. Your flippers will propel you through the water pretty fast and I'm a strong swimmer; I can save you if you start to drown."

"I barely swim," I answered. "I'll give it a try." I kept worrying that I would disappoint her; after all she had spent a lot of money on this trip, and I knew snorkeling was important to her. Off we started. I was amazed at the help the flippers gave me, and we truly did glide through the water. It didn't take long to be so caught up with the underwater panorama that I forgot my ineptness at swimming.

Nothing prepares you for some moments in life. Seeing the underwater world—a reef and the sea life it sustains—for the first time was an experience I'll never forget. The colors were spectacularly brilliant, almost neon. It seemed not only was I seeing colors and hues previously unknown to me, but new kinds of vegetation and creatures as well. It was a whole new world I hadn't even known exists.

We must have seen hundreds of types of fish. Joy wore a waterproof card attached to her wrist that helped us identify the various marine species—from octopus to flounder, from needlefish to barracuda and parrot fish. We managed to *talk* underwater through the air tubes.

" ... orn ih," Joy would say as she pointed to a colorful, nubby fish and then to the corn fish on the card. Sometimes we stopped, stuck our heads out of the water, pulled off our snorkels, and had a real conversation—and I didn't sink! I couldn't believe how buoyed up I felt, almost as if a magical power was undergirding me. I didn't even have to tread water.

"I can't believe I'm doing this," I said. "I really don't swim much at all. I have no idea why I'm not sinking." Joy's eyes went to the front of my bathing suit where the left side seemed to buoy up, practically under my chin. I glanced down as my thoughts caught up with hers.

"Do you think *that's* what's holding me up?" I pointed to my bosom. "Let's find out!" With one swoop I grabbed my prosthesis out of my bodice and tossed it in Joy's direction. The next thing I knew, I was going down as my "breast" was heading in the direction of South America.

Disregarding my mouthpiece, I gulped an enormous mouthful of saltwater before I remembered to use my trusty flippers to propel me back to the surface. I came up sputtering and frantically glanced toward shore, only to see hotels that looked like miniature markers from a Monopoly game, and sunbathers the size of gnats.

Fortunately, Joy was able to save me *and* my "breast," practically at the same time; by then, however, I was sure I couldn't possibly make it back to land.

How did I swim this far? I wondered as I held on for dear life to the artificial breast with both hands; *how will I ever get back to land?* Finally I managed to poke the prosthesis back in my bra and flail my way back. I fell face first in the sand and panted like a dog after a Frisbee game. I thought every breath would be my last; then it occurred to me that it would be far more dramatic to die snorkeling than to die of cancer.

The next day I was ready to try again. This time we went out on a dive boat; we would snorkel, then climb aboard for a rest, then snorkel again. We dove for conch, which the captain marinated and served with crackers; we swam with stingrays; and were frightened out of our wits by a shark, which the captain described as the largest he'd seen inside the reef. I could picture the headlines: "Nashville woman battles killer shark *and loses*." Again, it seemed more heroic than dying of cancer!

We walked the beach and gathered shells, talked, and gave each other facials. We fixed tuna salad one night, mashed potatoes and cooked carrots the next; the third, we visited the Grand Old House, where we ordered "one of each," and charged more than we should have to our American Express cards. That night we slept on the screened porch and awakened early to the crashing sounds of the ocean. The time went by all too fast!

Until my week in Grand Cayman, my whole psyche was an out-of-whack camera, and the image through the viewfinder was a blurred, distorted refraction of light and movement. Cayman was the repair shop that restored my capacity to focus. The vivid primary colors of the windsurfers against the greens of the ocean jumped at me. My sensitivities returned, and I can still remember the contrasting feelings in my body—skin burning hot from the driving sun and then tremulous shivers as I saturated myself with the chilling aloe lotion. The tingling, slightly painful peel of a facial mask brought back other forgotten sensations—the thudding of my heart against my innards as the shark swept through the waters; the ocean pulling me down, down, down; clinging to that stupid artificial breast and knowing I'd hang on as long as necessary because *I wanted to live.* These intense feelings became the talisman of my recovery!

There have been other trips to Cayman with other friends—once with our daughters. Hilarious times! But that first visit stands out as a milestone, almost as though I came back from the dead.

Another milestone of my recovery was the surprise party my friends gave to celebrate my five-year survival. Wayne and my invitation said, "Please come to a listening party for new recording artists, Sunday afternoon at 3:00." Little did I know the invitation was one-of-a-kind designed to throw me off the track. The rest of the guests received an invitation to a Celebrate Life! party in my honor. They were also invited to participate in an art show of sorts, and bring their personal collections or handiwork for display.

Dan and Phyllis had come from Chicago to spend the weekend with us—actually to attend the party—and I apologized to them for the interruption. "We're always having to go to listening parties, but we want you to go with us," I explained. "It may even be fun. You never know who will show up at these things."

As we walked through the door of the beautifully restored building on Second Avenue, cameras flashed in our direction, and I caught sight of banners proclaiming CELEBRATE LIFE! It took me a moment to realize I was looking into the faces of at least a hundred of my best friends who were cheering and smiling from ear to ear! As I turned to Wayne, the look on his face was priceless. He had known all along and had kept the secret!

A harpist played and several young friends clad in tuxedos served hors d'oeuvres, while Wayne and I tried to take it all in.

Many of my friends had been there all day hanging the gallery and preparing for the party. The exposed brick of the old building was a perfect backdrop for Bob McConnell's works of art, Shana's black-and-white photography, and Leigh's oil paintings.

There was poetry by Suzanne Gaither, and a large poster that proclaimed SUE-SATIONAL! from my friend Arch, a public relations executive. Mindy displayed a piece of her marbleized furniture.

From Doug and Laura Oldham there were framed pictures from another creative party we had shared years before, the Turkey Awards, at which gold turkeys were given to some of the top names in music for their best-left-untold, most embarrassing moments.

There was a wall hanging that said Celebrate Life! and a matching T-shirt from Bill and Gloria, and a hand-embroidered and appliquéd sweatshirt with the same motif from Kay. Joy and Peggy stood proudly beside their creation—a life-size op-art junk sculpture which looked better than some of the things I've seen in the Metropolitan Museum of Modern Art! Joy had also made a seascape panorama, complete with sand and seashells, that had a little plastic image of me in my pink bathing suit made from an actual photograph. Minnie's display was a bikini-torso cake just like the one she made when I was in the hospital.

We oohed and aahed and stuffed ourselves with Marty's gourmet delights. Then just when it seemed too good to be true, the crowd turned hostile! They roasted me! One by one they told their stories and poked good-natured fun at me. My brother Jon showed a video he had edited to the song, "She's Got Personality." He used footage that made me want to crawl under the rug!

A group of my professional musician friends sang a song they had written called, "She Did Her Very *Breast*!" and presented me with a T-shirt with those words. And if this weren't enough, there were gifts for me and for Wayne too—it was his birthday. The afternoon ended with some serious moments of singing and joy. Our smile muscles ached.

Several years later, we celebrated another significant milestone. This time, Wayne and I threw the party, and our friends and relatives came from all over the country. It wasn't officially in honor of my ten-year survival, yet as we made our plans, I couldn't help think about it.

Officially, it was the celebration of our daughter's wedding. It was "love at first sight" for Dana and Barry after twelve years of being each other's best friend.

Barry's mother, Bonnie, and I tease them that we knew years ago when they were in college, it was a perfect match. We remind them of how we kept our mouths shut and didn't try to interfere. Through the years we watched them console each other through many failed romances, and we observed they were obviously happier together than at any other time.

At last, "after much prayer and fasting on the part of the mothers" (Bonnie's words), Dana turned around as Barry came toward her on the ski slope, and their hearts did flip-flops. The wedding was everything we could have dreamed of.

There was glorious congregational singing accompanied by pipe organ and trumpet. Barry's pastor's wonderful prayer called on God to set this moment apart for His intended purpose. Then when Dana's pastor, who was conducting the ceremony, asked Wayne the typical question about " . . . who gives this woman to be married to this man?" Wayne surprised us with a speech he had prepared for just this moment. He moved in front of Dana and spoke first directly to her:

> Dana, this is a wonderful moment for your mother and me. Soon after you were born, we presented you to God, asking Him to use your life for His glory. Later . . . you determined with all your heart to be obedient and to follow Him. This has made your mother and me proud of you and very thankful.

Then turning to Barry he continued:

> . . . and Barry, you too were dedicated to God by your parents. You, like Dana, long ago decided to live for God.

Then he reached and took Barry's hand and joined it to Dana's:

> In obedience to God, Sue and I give our daughter to you, Barry. We entrust to your safekeeping her spiritual and physical well-being. Your parents join us in giving our blessing to you and Dana, knowing that you'll be continuing a heritage each of the four of us have been privileged to have . . . a Christian home.
>
> Now let the celebration begin!

It was a high moment in a glorious service.

After the wedding and reception—a party with elegant food and a great band—friends and relatives from both families changed into casual clothes and came to our house for the evening. My dear friend and right arm, Bea, helped me serve a buffet dinner; then we all crowded into our family room to sing around the piano. From raucous hand-clapping songs to "Amazing Grace," the harmony was magnificent.

Someone suggested a solo from Miles, Barry's dad who is an accomplished musician. Next we had an impromptu male quartet, then a piano solo from cousin Matt, followed by a number by the Hines family, and on and on. My cousin's wife, Rita, played with flair any song that was mentioned, including accompanying Peggy's rowdy performance of "I'm Jest a Girl Who Cain't Say No!" from the musical, *Oklahoma*.

As the evening drew to a close, there was still one song to be sung. It would be the rousing old gospel song that had ended our family gatherings long ago. As I looked into the faces of Nancy and Jim, my cousins, I was momentarily transported back to their parents' farm in southern Ohio where we, the city cousins, visited the country cousins. I could almost see their parents—Dewey in his bib overalls and Chrissy with her mandolin in her lap—and the faces of my mother and daddy. I could almost hear all of us singing; in memory, our harmony was perfect!

Now here we were so many years later with our husbands, wives, children, and friends. *This must be a little hint of what heaven will be like*, I thought to myself; *just so much joy, we can hardly contain ourselves!* As if on cue, Rita struck a chord and we sang

There's going to be a meeting in the air.
In the sweet, sweet by and by . . .

fourteen

A Yellow Convertible and a Pink and Black Ford

$\mathcal{A}$ Life-threatening experience makes you look at life in an entirely new light. You become a philosopher, a theologian, a poet. You want to know where you came from, why you're here, and why you are the way you are.

What is truth? you ask. *What can I really stake my life on?* You examine the things you've been taught and try to sort truth from myth. You wonder about your roots, your history. *Who were those ancestors in the sepia-toned pictures? What genetic characteristics were transmitted down the bloodline to me? What strengths? What weaknesses? What dispositions? Predispositions?*

There is a new dichotomous perspective to your examinations. You find you are more outgoing, yet more introspective. More fearful, yet more daring. On one hand you cling more tightly to your loved ones; on the other, you release them, knowing your hold is temporal.

In many ways you are more open. You reach out to others, are more gregarious; yet at the same time you hold back, are more private. Sometimes you seem to be looking at the world from a safe distance rather than actually participating in it.

After my chemotherapy was finished, I was overwhelmed that it was over and that I was alive. I seemed to view the world in the terms of my trade, photography. I wondered if any other living person saw what I saw, felt what I felt—experienced it so deeply. My journal entries from that time reflect my feelings.

- Today I see a paper sculpture as I look across the landscape—monochromatic grays, not a color in sight. Before I would have said, *Such a gray, gray day.* Today I say, *If it were possible to capture this, I could sell it to a king.*

- The whole weekend was filled with color and motion ... high-speed film motion! Even with the proper film there could possibly be a blur ... horizontally across the image. Perhaps the blur would add to the magic.

- The sky is bluer than blue, as though you are using your polarizing filter to the max. The clouds move like shadow dancers—like visible spirits looking for a place to light. Spirits can't be photographed.

- It's the magic hour—the only perfect time of the day for a photographer, when the daytime glare is gone, and there are no harsh shadows ... just before dusk (or right after dawn if you're up!). If you shoot fast, *right now*, the pictures will be incredible in the magical lighting.

- Rain ... summer rain! With slow-speed film I could record each drop and each water-laden leaf and flower ... drooping almost to the ground.

- Construction workers ... with ecru skin, in yellow hats ... bright yellow like daffodils ... their tools a creative milieu on the ground around them. Hold that shot, guys!

- It's a dull, dreary day they say. Dear God—it's a day! It's brittle maybe ... winter brittle ... but there are tinges of gold and magenta off in the distance. And there are patterns! Patterns etched in the sky and on the ground. It could be shot in color ... subtle and pale. Perhaps black and white is better ... to do justice to the patterns!

- With a tripod I could capture the lightning. To a photographer's mind, life swirls like those thunderheads in the distance.

Not only did I feel the need to philosophize, but I wanted desperately to go home—back to Charleston, West Virginia, and retrace my steps. It probably had nothing to do with my illness;

more likely my age. I've noticed that my husband and my friends have the urge to return to where they came from.

Joy went back to Petoskey, Michigan, for a visit right out of the blue. She looked up all of her mother's friends and went to the church her father pastored when she was a teenager.

Wayne loves to go back to Dana, Indiana, every chance he gets. He drives through the countryside and visits his friends. "That's where the high school was," he says with pride, "right on that empty lot by the Methodist church." He tells me where Overpeck's store was and where Hammersleys had their gas station. In a couple hours' time, he can take me on a tour of the whole town and remind me that all of it was his paper route once upon a time. (Anyone else could give the tour in six minutes flat.)

Even before the announcement came for my high school reunion, I'd been thinking about going to Charleston. Not only did I want to go to Daddy's grave, but I was feeling sentimental about people and places.

"Fasten your seat belts, and bring your seat backs to an upright position for landing," the flight attendant's voice orders. "We'll be on the ground in Charleston momentarily." I press my nose to the window and see nothing.

I remember when this airport was built. They took the tops from three mountains and filled in the valleys. "Do you think the pilot can hit the runway?" my seatmate asks. "If he misses, it's a long way down." I remember someone asking me that exact question years ago when I flew in from college and then again when I came home with a pink bundle in my lap.

We're circling. (Perhaps he's getting up his nerve.) "I guess the pilot has to hit the runway, no matter where it is," I answer.

A thousand thoughts flash through my mind. Whatever happened to Margarite and Capey? Did Capey ever build his television set? I think of Clurey and the kids I played with on Sixth Street—Lee and Francie, the Jones kids, the Liebles, and Bucky Rutledge . . . Hide and Go Seek in the lumberyard . . . helping ourselves to watermelons from boxcars on the railroad siding.

I close my eyes and wonder about the reunion. Will we know each other? Could it really have been thirty years? I smile at the thought of the black silk Christian Dior (designed to show just a hint of my newly created bosom) carefully folded in tissue paper in my suitcase.

The next morning, by light of day, I look out the window and try to get my bearings. My hotel, a Marriott high-rise, seems to stand on the spot of the old Union Mission where I went as a child to hear the Fisk Jubilee Singers and see Marjoe, the boy evangelist.

Clusters of townhouses, strange new towers of glass and steel, have replaced dismal slum-like buildings and there's a shopping center smack in the middle of town! The state capitol with it's gold-leafed dome, the most beautiful in the nation, shines brightly in the sunlight.

My car heads for Sixth Street, back to my childhood home. I giggle as I pass Sacred Heart Church, remembering Mrs. Vandertweezers and her close call with Father Cuthbert.

The nerve of them to close Jolly's, the little grocery store where we stood in line for hours to buy bubble gum! (Those were war years and bubble gum was almost impossible to get.) Sixth Street Methodist Church, where we attended early on, looks just as it did. So does Bucky Rutledge's house. I remember the scarlet fever quarantine signs nailed to those pillars; signs put there by the city as a warning to all who passed. Scarlet fever! Those were dreadful words. How it frightened our mothers.

They cured that, I think, *and TB, and polio! Someday there will be a cure for cancer.*

It's hard to figure out which house is mine. I have to count back from the corner. One . . . two . . . three. The old porch must have fallen down. A new facade is in its place. The house is so much smaller than it used to be!

The house on Mathews Avenue, where we lived next, will be easy to spot . . . that pretty white house with the picket fence, and the pink dogwood tree . . . big awning over the porch with comfortable furniture and blooming pots (I can actually picture myself sitting in the glider with Ray Harbour). Maybe I've come back to find my youth.

The description is only in my memory! I'm angry! Angry because time simply refused to stand still! My house is *pink!*—the worst shade of pink I've ever seen. The fence is gone. The dogwood is gone. Ray is gone. And the house is *so small*. It shrank!

Shall I knock on the door and see what they've done to the innards of my house? Is it pink inside too? Is the breakfast nook there? How about the bedrooms that fit up under the slant of the roof? I glance at the grass growing high between the cracks in the driveway.

That's where Wayne asked for my hand in marriage, I think, and it makes me smile. We were sitting in the car with my parents, having just returned from church. *I want to marry your daughter . . .* seems like I can almost hear Wayne's voice. Then silence! Dead silence! *Daddy, say something!* The memory makes me laugh.

Wouldn't it be funny if Daddy's gourds are still growing up over the garage? I wonder and impulsively decide to check it out. No gourds are visible, but I'm delirious that the vine is still there. It dawns on me someone might look out the window and wonder what I'm doing here—why I'm laughing.

I vow that this house where I was nurtured and loved will remain white and lovely, and big! . . . the fence and dogwood in place. I drive the route to my best friend's house and come back and drive my old route to Woodrow Wilson Junior High School. It's closed, boarded up like a ghost town. I drive to Stonewall Jackson High School and discover it's now a technical school.

The first night of my high school reunion (a two-night event) I was given a name tag with a picture that couldn't possibly have been me, a skinny-necked brunette with pointy, horn-rimmed glasses. There was noisy brouhaha as we examined each other's pictures. We nerdy little people turned out to be fine-looking adults after all.

A hand-lettered sign caught my eye: IN MEMORY OF . . . and there was a picture of Johnny Hull, the class clown. "Suicide," my friend said, and my eyes skim the names and photos till they rested on three pictures side by side; three of my best girlfriends.

"All three died of breast cancer," someone told me, and my thoughts go wild wondering what we all did, what we unknowingly exposed ourselves to. Was it coincidence, nothing more? It dampened my spirit.

The next morning I awakened early. Betty, my father's beautiful, forever-young cousin, had promised to go with me to the cemetery. Her mother and daddy, Mae and Elmer, are buried near Daddy. I was glad I didn't have to be alone. It made me sad to know my parents didn't rest together side by side. I thought of Mother in that sandy, lonely, unshaded grave in Lantana, Florida . . . home of the *National Enquirer*! I laid my rose on Daddy's lonely grave.

The second night was a dinner and dance. The committee had worked hard, dug up film from our senior picnic, organized the cheerleaders and majorettes for a routine, bought prizes for those with the most children, the person coming the farthest distance, etc. And the person most changed . . . *me!*

There were mini-reunions around the room. We listened to the band and danced. There were pictures being shown, bragging about children and grandchildren, and about successes. For a few there have been no successes since the pass that won the football game long ago.

Shall I go back for my fortieth reunion? We'll have to wait and see how the face-lift turns out!

On Sunday morning as I dressed for church, I wondered how it would be. As I drove the winding road to the new location I wondered how I would feel. Would the legalism that I remembered, and that seemed to enslave us, be prevalent? Would I be sorry I came?

My heartbeat quickens as I pull into the parking lot. The building is beautiful, just like a *real* church—steeple, stained glass, and all. The service is formal but not stuffy, not the free-for-all I remembered. The music is magnificent. I see new faces, young families, children everywhere, and well-dressed women with up-to-date hairdos! Tastefully made-up faces! I see people I remember from my youth, older but the same, and they are as happy to see me as I am to see them.

One thing is the same—exactly the same! Everyone has a Bible, and when a Scripture is mentioned, you can hear the rustle of pages turning like leaves blowing in the wind! I feel God's presence and my heart is overflowing with gratitude. Somehow I had confused the man-made rules and notions with truth. Now I know the difference.

I had opportunities for other reunions over the next couple of years, one with my college friends and another with my high school friends. Until our high school reunion, I hadn't seen Carlene for years. That night she, her husband Jack, and I sat together at dinner.

"We should get the trio together," Carlene suggested. That night we made plans to call Janet, the other member of our trio, and see what we could work out. Janet and I had stayed close through the years, calling each other often, and exchanging greeting cards. Once in a while, I was in Dallas on business and stayed at her house.

That fall began a yearly get-together of "The Trio," a bit misleading, since there are four of us. Susie took my place in the group when I went off to college; thus she qualifies as a genuine member.

The four of us meet, trying to synchronize our arrivals at the Dallas airport, drive a couple of hours east to a beautiful horse ranch with a picture-perfect guest house, where we settle in for a long weekend. Each day we make our way to First Monday in Canton, Texas, which is perhaps the world's largest flea market of antiques, teddy bears, Christmas clothing, handmade gifts, and foods. We spend three full days there and never manage to see it all.

At night we talk about old boyfriends and the cars they drove—Eddie Starkey and the old rattletrap Chevy, Gary Monday and the yellow convertible, Ray Harbour and his pink and black Ford; about Fred Cook, Bob Grishaber, and Wesley (we-forget-his-last-name), and Jackie, whom Carlene did, in fact, marry.

We talk about the girls we hated way back then, and Susie can still imitate Mitzy's suh-weet little whiny voice: "It's just an ol' blanket," she says. "Why, just last night my mama took an ol' blanket off the bed and made this skirt. It's just an ol' blanket." We laugh till we cry and then discuss whether Mitzy and Nicky could possibly still be happy together after all these years. Someone points out that he'd probably have been happier with me. I didn't ever *want* Nicky; I just didn't want Mitzy to have him! "Sure! Sure!" they say.

Little did we know when we were together one November that Janet's husband, Jim, was consumed with cancer and would be dead within seven weeks. As he did every year, he snapped our picture before we left for the airport. He looked pale and complained of a pain in his side.

We returned for his memorial service and to walk by Janet's side and scatter his ashes around the lake where he and I fished (when I was bored with shopping). I couldn't help but wonder why it had to happen.

This is Dallas, I thought, *a city known for its medical centers. Will there ever be a cure for this disease?* This question hung over my head like a cloud as I boarded the plane for Nashville.

fifteeɴ

A Quest for the Nobel Prize

Aᴜɴt ᴇᴅɴa, my aʟᴛᴇʀ eɢo, often jokes about the medical profession. "My doctor complained because my check came back. I told him, 'So what? So did my arthritis!'"

Aunt Edna aside, it's no secret how we feel about doctors. Most of us have a love/hate relationship with them. We love them because we believe they know the secrets that will make us whole. Still, we are mad because it's a nuisance to have to go to them, it's expensive, and let's face it, we're insecure because *they know more than we do!* It's a mystery to me that we can feel so secure in almost every area of our lives and yet feel so insecure with doctors.

For me, it's like going to McDonald's. I stand there in line saying my order over and over in my head, so I won't embarrass myself when I get to the front of the line—Big Mac, small fries, a cup of water, and chocolate chip cookies. Likewise, I sit there half-naked in the examination room reciting my symptoms over and over in my head like a third grader who is scared of her teacher!

I'm sure people in the medical profession have their insecurities too; it's just that most of the time they don't let them show. Some time ago I told my dentist how much I enjoyed my visits to his office and how I looked forward to talking to him. I thought the poor man was going to cry. "No one has ever said that to me before. Usually, my patients say, 'You're the last person I wanted

167

to see today!'" He explained that after a while you want to quit; you just can't take it anymore. His words were prophetic.

One day I called his office and found the number was no longer in service. Later I saw him in a store dressed in shabby clothes and with long unkempt hair. "I'm a dropout from society," he told me. "I'm working in the mountains of Tennessee in a program that provides free dental care to poor children. They really like me!" He told me he had never been happier.

I'll never forget Dr. Joe Selman, who brought me into the world and took care of our family until he died. He was a giant of a man with a gentle soul. We could *drop in* for a visit in his downtown office, or he would come to the house. Dr. Joe was right up there close to God when it came to respect. "He probably has more patients than anyone in town, but he never shortchanges you," Mother would say. And as though she were announcing some specialty for which he had trained, she would add, "He practices commonsense medicine."

The last time I saw Dr. Joe was on a visit back to Charleston when Dana was two and was suffering from an earache. "Honey, I can prescribe something for those ears, but from what you tell me, she's been living on antibiotics for the last two years. Maybe it would be best to let her little immune system begin working on its own. Let's just watch her closely and keep her fever down. Besides, I hate to stick needles in these sweet little bottoms," he said as he patted hers. I took his advice and Dana never had another ear infection.

Sometime between my childhood and that of my children, the family doctors who knew us, loved us, and communicated with us either disappeared, or at best, became few and far between. To me, the words *know* and *communicate* are like the song "Love and Marriage," they "go together like a horse and carriage."

I know a lot of doctors socially, others I know through business connections; but it's hard these days to find one who wants to *know* me when I'm his patient. I don't want to have lunch with him or go to his kid's bar mitzvah; I just want him to know me as a person instead of a malady—a bone, a heart, or a tumor. "Hey, nurse! Pull the file on that cancer with the blonde hair!"

After so many years of listening to women talk about their problems with doctors, it occurred to me that I might work toward solving the dilemma not only for myself, but for all humankind. By doing so, I might be eligible for the coveted Nobel Peace Prize.

My first thought was what I would wear to accept my award. Next, I took out a piece of paper and made two columns. In the first I wrote, "What Medical People Can Do," and in the second, "What Patients Can Do." So far, so good!

Next I gathered my data. I began close to home with my sister-in-law, Becky, who is a radiology technologist. She not only keeps me supplied with articles on diagnostic techniques and other interesting things about the cancer industry, but I can count on her to help me think things through.

I talk to her almost every day. Sometimes I have an excuse, to get a recipe or to find out what she does to make her pansies bloom so well. Most of the time I call simply because I need a *Becky fix!* She is levelheaded and calm—two things I'm not—and I've learned to depend on her wise and thoughtful judgment.

"I'm going to ask you a question; tell me the first thing that pops into your head," I said when Becky answered the phone. I took the silence to mean she was waiting eagerly for the question. "What's the one thing a patient could do to make your job easier?" I didn't think my question funny, yet I could barely hear Becky's answer through her laughter.

"Take a bath!" she giggled. "Sometimes I have a patient who smells so bad I'm tempted to hold my nose with one hand and x-ray him with the other."

"So whadaya do?" I asked.

"You do the same thing you do when you change dirty diapers; you breathe through your mouth!" We both had a good laugh. After I hung up I wrote a poem and faxed it to Becky's office.

This lim'rick is straight from your docs;
Sometimes when you take off your sox,
The smell is so awful
It's almost unlawful.
We think we are treating an ox.
The doctors present this petition;
"Don't come in a dirty condition.
Wash the parts of your bod,
Or honest to God,
We'll not want to be your physician."
An unclean patient coerces
A doctor to tantrums and curses.
He'll sure go berserk
And act like a jerk
And perhaps take it out on his nurses.
Don't spray yourself down with perfume
Cause *you* like it, please don't assume!
One person's smell
Is another one's hell,
He might dread coming into the room.
When you're in that small room and it's close-ed
And your parts are all out there expose-ed,
If the odor is rotten,
To the morgue you'll be gotten
Cause your body has smelled decompose-ed.
We've all had mothers, I conject,
Giving unwanted advice. Correct?
The one thing they all say
(From now until doomsday,)
"Change your underwear,
you might be in a wreck!"

Mothers have been saying that last line almost as long as they've been telling us not to kiss the cat lest we get a horrible disease. I personally have never heard of a person in a horrible wreck, being pried free by the "Jaws of Life," loaded on the stretcher, blood-soaked beyond recognition, and of hearing an ambulance attendant say, "Look at this poor girl's underwear. I don't believe she's changed it for a couple of days."

I'm not saying it never happened; but if so, I haven't heard about it. It could be it's the main topic of conversation at the National Ambulance Driver's Convention.

After striking out with Becky, it occurred to me that if I interviewed a thousand physicians and asked them what the *patient* could do to bring about a better doctor/patient relationship, I would get a thousand different answers, everything from "Stop hanging my diplomas and pictures upside down!" to "Pity me! How would you like to go through life hearing your mother brag about 'my son the doctor' when what you really wanted to be was a country singer?"

If you asked a thousand patients what the *doctor* could do to improve the relationship, you would get a thousand answers, the most repeated one being, "He could read *Good Housekeeping*! After all, that's where I picked up on *my* symptoms—really! Good doctors will run each other down getting to the newsstand to find out the latest maladies and their cures, so they'll know what we're talking about!"

Ten years ago, after my mastectomy, when I was frantically making the rounds and the phone calls to gather information, I called a shirttail relative of Mother's in Colorado. (Actually, we aren't sure about the shirttail or even if there really is a connection at all.)

My phone call to Dr. Marvin Burnett was one of the most significant things I did. Marvin had the unique ability to take my jumbled thoughts and help me make sense of them. I spoke to him several times over the next few weeks, and while he didn't give me any earth-shattering new information, I always put down the phone with a better understanding of the strange new things that were going on in my life. Often when we talked, the conversation turned into a good-natured sparring match on the subject of doctor/patient communication.

"Marvin, let's solve it once and for all. Let's write down what medical professionals should expect from patients and vice versa, box it, and sell it on the street corner." I didn't tell him about my dream of the "Nobel!" (I didn't want to share the glory unless I had to.)

"Sue, I've told you before, and I'm tellin' you again, there's no formula . . . there are no lists." I could hear the how-many-times-do-I-have-to-tell-you implications coming through the phone line. Then he said, "Get on a plane and come out here; follow me around a couple of days. Meet the people I work with, talk with my patients, and then you'll know." We spoke again several days later; once again Marvin urged me to come to Denver.

I had no intentions of going to Denver. I certainly enjoyed a good chat with Marvin now and then, but if I was going to use the free plane ticket in my desk drawer, it would be to talk to a person on my *hotshot* list, someone I'd seen on television or read about in the news.

However, one of Marvin's comments kept replaying in my mind, and the more times I heard it, the more it made sense. "You know, Sue, about ten percent of docs are the biggies—the media types—the ones you read about or see on television. Maybe about five or ten percent are the bad guys, the ones who are doing what they do for the wrong reasons. And the rest of us, you know what we are? We're just journeymen. We work hard. We aren't after recognition. We are simply busy caring for people. Sue, you need to know what the journeymen are doing. Come on out here."

I thought about Marvin's invitation often over the next few days and finally had my secretary book the flight.

This is probably a wild goose chase, I thought as I drove from the Denver airport. *Even if it is, I'll enjoy all this beauty. Where else can I see the flowering trees of spring against a backdrop of snowcapped mountain peaks?*

The next morning at the break of dawn, Marvin, coffee cup in hand, picked me up in his Jeep. He called it his "Colorado Cadillac." We chatted as he dodged traffic on our twenty-minute trip to downtown Denver.

"You have free reign to talk to people—office staff, nursing staff, patients. Ask questions, observe, absorb. That's what you're here for—to absorb."

He glanced at me from under the Rockies baseball cap he wore to keep his hair from blowing in the breeze from the sunroof. "When this day is over, you'll at least know the answer to one of your questions: What should a person expect from his doctor?" I want you report back to me at the end of the day and tell me what you learned.

Gee, I didn't know there would be a quiz, I thought as we pulled into the parking garage. We made our way along the corridors to his office. I plugged in my laptop computer; he filled his coffee cup.

"I get a card and a letter every year from a patient who was diagnosed with granulocytic leukemia when her son was born. I guess he's sixteen years old now." Marvin was shuffling through his desk. "I treated her at that time. She's been in remission all these years—chromosome cure. The disease doesn't even show up in the chromosomes." I assumed Marvin's desk shuffling meant he was looking for the letter to prove his case.

Finally, he gave up, leaned back in his chair, and smiled a satisfied smile. "That's the hole-in-one! That's why you come back the next day!" He looked at his watch, stood, and moved towards the door. "And Sue, remember this: the person with cancer isn't a different person from before he had cancer. He is the very same person. The body is just the monument to the person. I can treat the disease, but I can't touch the you *of you*." He stepped into the hallway, then stuck his head around the door. "And oh, by the way, don't forget, I want to know what answers you've found to your questions."

With that he headed down the hall to see his first patient. *Yeah and I want naturally blonde hair too!* I said to myself.

The nurses in the lab were busy preparing for patients, but they invited me into the cramped space. "You can come in but your coffee cup can't. Those are government rules, not ours." We introduced ourselves.

"We were just talking about the support group that was started last week," said Joyce, a classy-looking woman with fashionably cut hair, maroon glasses, and a big smile. "It's something we've really needed."

"Oh yes," I agreed wholeheartedly. "I'm a believer in support groups. I've seen them work for hundreds of patients."

"Not them! Us!" Joyce laughed as she fooled with the gauges on a machine. Then she turned to look at me; even though she was smiling, I could see the pain in her eyes. "We do have support groups for patients, but we've just begun a support group for *us*, to help us deal with *our* grief. We get so attached to our patients that when we lose one—and we do lose them—we need to talk about it. We need a chance to cry. Matter of fact, the other night at the meeting, there wasn't a dry eye in the place."

This was new to me. I thought medical people were supposed to hold their patients at arm's length and not become emotionally involved.

Marvin's philosophy came in bits and pieces. Each time after he saw a patient, he found me and offered another observation. "Ya know, Sue, after the diagnosis, the first thing a doctor should do is treat a person for shock. Remember what you learned when you were a Girl Scout? Treat the person for shock. We rarely begin medication on the first visit. We talk to them, listen to them, assure them. We treat 'em for shock." With that, Marvin hustled down the hall to another patient.

"Another thing, you don't try to make a patient a medical student." It was as though he hadn't left the room. Marvin had the knack of picking up right where he left off, almost in the middle of a sentence. "You give her the truth, but you don't ram it all down her throat at once. It's like telling your children about sex. You tell them as they ask. That's what you do with a patient—you answer her questions today; then you answer her questions tomorrow, and the next and the next. Yeah, that's a lot of phone calls, a lot of time on our part," he said as though he read my mind, " . . . but that's what we're here for." Again he disappeared into an examination room.

The next time Marvin appeared it was to motion me to follow him. "Come on and go with me." I wasn't sure I was ready to meet a patient, but I didn't have time to think about it. Suddenly I was being introduced to Leigh, a breast cancer patient not much older than Mindy, and her mother who was visiting from the East.

"Leigh has had a bone marrow transplant. That's why she's wearing a mask . . . has to guard against infection." I knew that in younger women with breast cancer the procedure was to take out bone marrow, treat it intensively to eradicate the tumors, then re-fuse it.

As Marvin checked his patient my eyes were glued to the mother. Her body language and the pain in her beautiful face told the story well. If she could not take the place of her desperately sick daughter, then she would *feel* every horrible moment with her. Even as the doctor prodded the inside of Leigh's mouth with his tongue depressor, the mother's mouth worked the same con-tortions as that of her child.

When Marvin finished his examination, he sat down and he and Leigh had a typical doctor-patient dialogue: "How have you been feeling?" . . . "Have you been unusually tired?" . . . "How's your appetite?" . . . "No, it's probably not a good idea to go to a rock concert this weekend because of the chance of infection. Your white count is just too low."

Marvin stood to his feet and laid his hand gently on Leigh's arm. "I'll be back in a minute. The results of the blood work should be ready. I'll check . . . be right back." He gave her arm a squeeze. "I really think the concert is out, regardless. Sorry 'bout that."

When the door closed behind him, Leigh turned her tired eyes to her mother. "Did you see that, Mom? Did you see him put his hand on my arm. Did you see him touch me?" The mother had noticed; she had felt it too.

The news Marvin brought back wasn't good. He rattled off numbers that both women understood. "Why hasn't it come up yet? I've talked to two other patients who had bone marrow trans-plants and the blood count came right back."

Marvin sat down and thought a moment. "Well, how many times have you seen a pregnant woman and she tells you she's overdue, and everybody keeps asking, 'Why hasn't it come? I don't understand.' Well, it's just not ready. It will come, though, and that's what I think about your blood count—it'll come when it gets ready. Just takes longer for some people. We have more tricks in the bag . . . we'll do a booster if we have to. That will stimulate the bone marrow to produce white cells. For now, Leigh, let's just take it a day at a time."

"You talk a little bit, you listen a little bit," Marvin told me in the hallway. "Matter of fact, if you let a patient talk long enough, she'll tell *you* what is wrong."

"In that case, Marvin, I could be a doctor!"

I was surprised at how the time had flown. Before leaving for a hospice meeting, Marvin arranged for me to have lunch with Sharon, the office manager, and Ginny who is in charge of the nursing staff. As we waited for the elevator, we couldn't help but overhear the uncontrollable sobs of a woman using a pay phone. Her face was pressed tightly against the wall so as to not draw attention to herself.

"We've got to do something about that. People need privacy at a time like that." I could see Ginny making a mental note to find a place for patients to make phone calls in privacy.

As we sat down to eat, I commented on the fact that between the two of them, Ginny and Sharon seemed to be aware of everything that went on. "Some people would have missed the lady in the hallway. After all, it must happen every day in medical offices all over the country."

"Our antennae are always up," Sharon responded. "That's our number one job—to make it easier for the patient."

During lunch I learned that making it easier for the patient meant everything from coming in early in the morning to helping someone get to work on time (even on a Saturday morning when patients normally aren't scheduled), to calling a cab for someone too sick to drive. "We have a tab with the cab company.

If a patient calls and says he can't come in, that he's too weak to drive, we say, 'You need to be here—a cab is on the way.'"

"We also have a tab at a nearby restaurant. If a patient has to wait for tests or for reports to come back, or because we just can't get to them, we buy their lunch. No one says, 'Should we arrange for that couple to have lunch? They've been here a long time.' It's just understood. It's taken care of."

After lunch I poked my head into a small cubbyhole, where a young woman worked alone. Taped along the edges of her computer screen were baby photos. I stood admiring the pictures for a few minutes, not knowing if I should interrupt. "That's my baby," the young woman offered as she turned from her screen. "Two months old! I'm Karen. I'm the study coordinator. I'm doing research."

With a little prompting, I was able to find out the answer to a question that I had wondered about for years: *How do doctors keep up with information?*

"We're connected into everything we need: pharmaceutical studies, the National Cancer Institute, universities . . . anything and everything in cancer research. I'm continually moving around in the computer world. If one of the doctors has a patient with a particular tumor he tells me, 'Get in there and get the new studies.' I work with the patients too. I tell them about new studies, and if they qualify, I give them an opportunity to participate. There might be a new protocol that is approved by the FDA but is still on trial. I keep track of the participants and feed that information into the computer too."

I thanked Karen for her time and walked out into the hallway.

All day I had been hearing about Libby Tracey. "Wait till you meet *her*," they told me. "I don't know if you're ready for *her*, she's a real character!" At lunch Ginny told me about Libby's first week on the job. It seems that Libby knew it was mandatory for a nurse who works in an oncology/hematology clinic to have a blood test. Even though she was a nurse, Libby could barely stand to draw a patient's blood, much less have her own taken. "I'm warning you," Libby told them, "I won't survive!"

The next day Ginny heard her name called over the loud-speaker ordering her to the lab: "STAT!" which means *quick*. There she saw Libby stretched out on the floor looking unconscious or worse! After a few seconds everyone burst into laughter, including the patients, who were in on the joke. From everything I was told, Libby kept the place hoppin'!

"Where is this person you've been telling me about?" I asked as I picked up the phone to call my office. "The day is almost over, the patients have gone home, and I've yet to meet this Libby person." As I was finishing my conversation with my secretary, suddenly out of nowhere appeared a tiny blonde dynamo of a person. She threw herself at me full force, hugged me like a linebacker, and plunked a kiss that hit halfway on my forehead and halfway in my eye.

When I hung up the phone one second later, she was nowhere to be found. Before I could get up from my chair, she was back, this time wearing a coolie hat and dragging along Malliah, a nurse I'd met earlier. "Let's sing for Sue." Malliah is a musician who performs and records with her gospel singing family, but the only similarity between Libby's performance and showbiz, as we know it, was the fact that she did look like a shorter Carol Channing.

Libby had been in class all day, her last class to complete a doctoral program in nursing; there was great speculation as to whether her associates would be required to call her *Doctor Nurse*. When I asked her what her role was, she answered, "I'm the cheerleader." It wasn't hard to imagine she was a key ingredient ... the person who bolsters not only the staff, but the patients as well.

"Gotta run to the hospital," she said, giving me another bear hug. "I'll be there late, but I'll be joining you at Marvin and Alison's for dinner." She was gone.

The office was quiet and Marvin motioned for me to sit down. "So, how 'bout it, Sue? Are you glad you came? Did you get your answers?" He sat with his elbows on his desk and his index fingers pointed like a church steeple at his chin.

"Yeah, Marvin. I had my answers by noon. It's so simple. What I want from you and your staff is exactly what I saw here today. I want someone to be happy my family member or friend has been free of leukemia for sixteen years, to call it a hole-in-one, and I want someone to be willing to go out of her way for me, maybe come in early so I can get to work on time. I want someone to notice that I need a quiet place for a phone call . . . maybe pay for my cab or lunch, not because I can't afford it, but to encourage me. And I'd love a cheerleader, a Libby, to make me laugh in the midst of my pain. And a touch! I wouldn't mind a touch . . . a hand on my arm now and then. And Marvin, do you know what the most comforting thought in the world would be?" He shook his head. "To know that someone would shed a few tears if they lost me."

"It's really simple, isn't it, Sue? What we want from each other is what we want from everyone: respect . . . kindness . . . and above all, caring. If we all had those, there wouldn't be a problem. Right?" Marvin rolled back his chair and stood to his feet. "Right!" He'd answered his own question. "Let's go home!"

sixteen

Dandruff, Cobwebs, and Lizard Spit

Not long after wayne and I moved to Nashville, we were invited to a party. Afterward someone asked, "How did you like mingling with country music stars?" Fortunately, I played it cool, I didn't say, "What country music stars?" The truth of the matter is, I had no idea we had been in the presence of stars!

The next day I decided that if I was going to live in "Music City," I would learn about the industry that brought it fame. I began by asking questions and reading brochures, and I visited the Country Music Museum. I even got on a tour bus and found out where the studios are and where the stars live.

Since that time, I've had the privilege of producing multi-image shows and videos for various music and music-related companies; we've also entertained a few "stars" in our home. Now I have such appreciation for country music that a couple of the buttons on my car radio are programmed to country stations. When I travel, the first thing I do when I get into my rental car is find the "twang!" Even when I was in South America for a video shoot, I listened to the "sounds of Nashville."

Where would country music be if it couldn't ask the question, Why? Why *did* he leave me? Why *doesn't* he leave me? Why'd she "do me wrong"? Why doesn't anything go right for me? And even, "Why me, Lord?" I wish I'd known about country music when I broke up with Ray Harbour and Jack Cromer. It certainly would have eased the pain!

Country music is where the rubber meets the road. It seems that just when life is going along at a pretty good clip, it happens—a severed relationship, a loved one with a drug problem, a business down the tubes, an illness, or even a death. The rain hits the crepe paper! Then come the questions: *Why my loved one? Why my business? Why didn't someone do something? Why me? Why now?*

I hear a lot of *whys* related to cancer, and I'd hoped to have all the answers before I got to the last chapter of this book. I had planned to get a couple of theological degrees and a Ph.D. or two in science. Perhaps I would become a medical doctor and get a graduate degree in fortune-telling. Maybe I'd spend a year in a monastery contemplating what I'd learned, and by then I would surely have the answers!

It didn't work out. First of all, there simply wasn't time for the educational process. As for the monastery, it doesn't allow Pizza Hut deliveries, time out to go to the beauty shop, or idle talk—which rules out the gossip I'm quite fond of!

One question I hear over and over in regard to cancer is, *Why can't they find a cure for this horrible disease?*

For one brief moment on a flight from Nashville to Chicago, I thought I would learn the answer to that question. That night I sat next to a distinguished-looking man, who spread papers and journals out all over his lap and the seat between us.

"You look busy! Sooo, what do you do? What's all this stuff?" I asked in my most cheerful voice.

He gave me a "drop dead" look over the top of his half-framed glasses. In his most don't-bother-me-lady-I-have-work-to-do voice, he said, "I'm a scientist, and I'm making a speech in Chicago." He edged his shoulder up and away, creating an invisible barrier between us.

I can take a hint! I got *my* stuff out of *my* briefcase and spread it out all over the place. So much for conversation en route to Chicago!

He shuffled papers for a couple of minutes, probably rethinking the situation, then said, "What do *you* do?"

For the next hour we talked; when we landed, he told me he traveled every week and had never before exchanged so much as a word with a fellow passenger. He said he couldn't believe how the time had flown. Of course!

Somewhere over Indiana, I asked him to tell me, from a scientist's point of view, where we stand in cancer research and when a cure will be found. "Don't use your scientist language," I said. "Tell me in words I can understand."

He leaned back, took a sip of his Bloody Mary, and thought a while. I could see him scrambling for an explanation my blonde head could understand. "Nowhere! We're nowhere," he said.

"It's like outer space, like going to another planet. It's not the getting there that's the problem. It's the fact that when you finally get there, you not only don't have maps, but you don't have roads. Even worse, the engineers are just beginning to survey and think things through. They're still trying to come up with first-draft blueprints."

He shut his eyes a moment. "Fact is, maybe we haven't yet arrived on the planet, much less begun to figure out where roads go and why."

Unlike my seatmate on the plane, another scientist, Dr. Martin J. Murphy, Jr., president and CEO of Hipple Cancer Research Center in Dayton, Ohio, sees the proverbial cup half full rather than half empty. Given the chance, he'll talk your leg off on the subject.

Erma Bombeck, who once followed Dr. Murphy at the dais, called him "a hard act to follow." He's animated, funny, and able to communicate his own compelling sense of urgency about cancer research. His perspective is not just that of a scientist, but that of a cancer patient as well.

"We're peeling away the onion," Dr. Murphy says with excitement, "layer after layer after layer." He tells me they are doing things, at least in the lab, that would have been considered science fiction four or five years ago.

I became acquainted with Dr. Murphy through his executive assistant, Bonnie Shafer, Dana's mother-in-law. At Bonnie's invitation,

I visited the Hipple Center and met some of the folks who are on the cutting edge of research. Each staff member stopped to welcome me and explain his or her niche in systematic scientific investigation. Everyone seemed every bit as thrilled about his or her place in the chain of progression as an astronaut would be about walking on the moon.

Dr. Murphy is optimistic about cures for cancer, and he is careful to speak in the plural. "Cancer is many diseases," he explains, "so we're talking about *cures*, not *a cure*."

It took a long time for that concept to sink in—to understand that it isn't one singular disease, like polio or TB—and that we will never find a vaccine that will wipe out all cancer once and for all. Cancer is like the weeds in my rock gardens.

The year we moved to Nashville, Wayne built two rock gardens for me. He dragged rocks from all over the property, stacked them neatly on a natural ledge in the backyard, and brought load after load of soil up the stone steps in a wheelbarrow. It was truly a labor of love.

In the spring and summer I can roll over in bed, look out the window, and admire the yellow daylilies, daisies, and those little purple flowers whose name I don't know. I like to sit on the back step with a glass of iced tea and take in the bed of begonias, impatiens, and a colorful variety of perennials and wildflowers.

Every spring after the tulips have finished their show, I pull on my gardening gloves, pick up my trowel, and begin weeding.

The problem I have year after year is that I still don't always know which are the wildflowers, which are the perennials, and which are the weeds. The annuals I have down pat! They are the ones I picked up at Farmers' Market yesterday!

If I wait too long to begin my yard work, the weeds, always greedy for nature's nutrients, will have become so thick and obnoxious that they will have taken over and the *keepers* will be puny. They may not even survive.

Like the weeds, cancer's nature is to multiply, take over the garden, and choke out the flowers—the healthy cells.

Cancer is like my weeds, too, in that there are so many varieties. According to Dr. Murphy, there are more than one hundred pathologically documentable kinds of cancer; and I've read that breast cancer in young women is actually a different disease from the one that attacks older women.

Even each person's cancer is different from the next and can differ in its resistance to drugs; for instance, whether or not a tumor has estrogen receptors makes a difference in its rate of growth.

"Should we find that evasive cure (the weed poison)," Dr. Murphy tells me, "it may be so toxic it will do more damage than good, seriously inhibiting the patient's ability to replenish the life-sustaining blood cells. Therefore, simultaneous with finding the 'magic potion,' they are searching for effective 'delivery boys' to take it to the site of the tumor or carry it through the blood stream to be absorbed by the cancer cells themselves."

One of the ways this is being done is by engineering cells that can deliver the toxic substances specifically to the site of a tumor. Perhaps this is what my scientist friend on the plane meant when he referred to building roads on some distant planet. This is good news to those of us who have suffered the side effects of chemotherapy and the barbaric way it is implemented—like buck-shot—get it out there and hope it hits something.

In the future it won't be necessary to poison the whole garden to get the weeds. We won't have to give the weeds a head start before we act, and they can be pinpointed and blasted, leaving the flowers strong to bloom and reproduce.

Until my visit to Hipple Cancer Research Center, my knowledge of science, from a class at Stonewall Jackson High School, and a because-you-have-to college lab, gave me an inaccurate mental picture of what really goes on in cancer research. I pictured white-coated men and women mixing up an assortment of stuff in test tubes and then calling in a group of volunteers to try the different potions to see which ones work.

I even wondered if scientists only thought in terms of chemicals. I wondered if they ever looked for cures in common things.

What if they mixed dandruff with cobwebs and the spit of a lizard? Imagine my surprise to learn that they *do* find answers in common things.

For instance, by studying how chickens lay eggs, scientists are learning about a condition that results in destruction of the bone and causes elevated levels of calcium in the blood. In knowing that, they have found a way to improve the patient's life and open a window for chemotherapy to treat the cancer itself.

As far as I know, there are no known cancer cures in lizard spit, but I met one doctor at Hipple, who is, in fact, experimenting with the newt, a close relative of the lizard, and is making some revolutionary discoveries. Years ago in that high school science class (or was it college?), we girls watched as the boys eagerly pulled the tails from newts. It took only a few weeks for the little guy to grow a new tail, just as science predicted!

The only approved method of controlling cancer today seems to be to kill malignant cells by surgery, chemotherapy, or radiation. But by studying the regenerative tissue of that tricky little critter, the newt, they are learning revolutionary applications that hold promise and hope for tomorrow's cancer patients.

Sometimes Dr. Murphy would go on a rampage of scientific gobbledygook, and I would have no idea what he was talking about. That was the case when he told me about genetic coding. I had to remind him to speak as though I were a sixth grader.

Gobbledygook aside, he's good with analogies. He compared the genetic coding of the human body to an orchestra. "If the composer, the maestro, and the musicians knew nothing about music and couldn't read it, couldn't even hear it in their heads, and couldn't play it, there would be cacophony!" Dr. Murphy wondered if the word *cacophony* was too much for a sixth grader and defined the word: "a meaningless mixture of crashing sounds."

"But," he continued, "once you understand the code, you can learn it and work with it. Then everything changes. It's then that music can be composed, played, engineered, and understood!"

Pausing again to take note of my juvenile level of understanding, he continued: "Just as with music, there's a system to genetic coding. If there is no understanding of it, there is chaos. When we understand it, however, we can play it, engineer it!" That excites my sixth-grade understanding! "Soon the *behavior* of cells, that makes them cancerous in the first place, can be isolated, identified, and engineered—*played*, if you will." Aha! I understood! The weeds can be destroyed while they are still dormant in the ground!

The question I keep asking is, "When? When will it happen?" The equivalent of four jumbo jet loads of Americans die every day from cancer. One in three of us has a reservation on one of those planes!

I am extremely distressed that in the fifteen years since my own cancer, there is very little "new news" when it comes to a clinical breakthrough. We seem to be doing a better job at prevention and early detection, but as to a "cure on the horizon," as far as I know, there is none.

I'm upset that so much has been spent on the cause of AIDS, a minuscule issue compared to the cancer pandemic. Surely we as Americans will join forces and demonstrate our collective will for changes in public policies and a rebalancing of the focus and funding of research. We must demand that we conquer cancer! *That's what we've always done in defeating every enemy that has threatened our nation.*

More and more as I travel around the country I meet cancer patients who have decided against clinical treatment, especially those methods considered invasive or toxic. Instead they've chosen unorthodox programs: regimens of vitamins; shark cartilage; coffee enemas; medical protocol not FDA approved and other rigmarole that would seem bizarre to most. Some claim to be cured; others believe their cancer has been arrested. In some cases, it's possible that it's simply *the believing* that brings about a cure. The mind is a strong tool and can work both positively and negatively for our health.

New trends are developing to access one's own health information—to find out for oneself. I believe we should examine all the possibilities. We should dig deep, apply great wisdom (cobwebs and lizard spit is not an option) and then use our God-given instincts to decide what is best for us. Taking responsibility for one's own body—one's own health issues—is a big step in the process.

Perhaps someday there will be a major breakthrough against this dreaded disease. Meanwhile, there probably isn't a cancer patient alive who hasn't had a good case of the *Why Me's?*—if not aloud in broad daylight, then surely during those long, dark hours of the night when he can't bring himself to elbow the loved one sleeping beside him or is too paralyzed to pick up the phone and cry out for help. I certainly have asked the *Why me?* question, not only in regard to my own illness, but to those of my parents as well.

Why did *my* parents have to die rather than our alcoholic neighbors who fought like alley cats? It wasn't that we were nosy—you would have had to be deaf to miss their Saturday night battles!

Our houses were close, and in the summer when the windows were open, we could hear every word *and* every smack of Tressy's butcher knife when it hit the stair steps as she crawled upward. "Charles, [smack] you [smack] ole son-of-a-——[smack] ... I'm gonna [smack] kill you. I'm comin' up [smack] to kill you [smack] right now" [double smack].

"She'll never kill him. They'll outlive us," Mother would say. "They're probably pickled, those two!" Mother was right; Tressy and Charles outlived both my parents by many years. *Why my parents? Why not those miserable neighbors?*

Peggy, years after Bob's death, still wonders, "Why Bob?" They adored each other. The question was evident in my hairdresser Pat's beautiful black eyes as she watched her Ronnie die from throat cancer. It's bound to be ringing in Janet's ears now that Jim is gone. At the memorial service I heard his fishing buddy Craig ask the question, "Why Jim? Look at all the people he counseled ... and his first book was just published! ... Why?"

I could see the question in my friend Betsy's eyes as she drifted in and out of consciousness after her diseased stomach was removed, and again even more intensely at Dana's wedding shower, when it occurred to Betsy she may not be around for her daughter Sara's wedding.

A day or two after my mastectomy, a strikingly beautiful woman with a halo of vivid red hair entered my hospital room. She introduced herself as Michelle, a friend of a friend, and gently described her own battle with breast cancer.

"You know, Sue, it was terrible to go through; but now as I look back, I believe I was *privileged* to have had this experience."

Privileged? I thought. *What a strange thing to say.* Michelle explained that her life had been in turmoil before this overwhelming interference but that the experience had changed everything. She described a new and vital relationship with God, a deeper love for her family, and a delight for life never before experienced.

A better, more sensitive and compassionate person maybe, but privileged? I thought. *No way!*

Different people seem to have different viewpoints on the *Why me?* question. My friend George Volkert, who died not long ago, was in property development. There are big red signs all over parts of Nashville that say "Southeast Venture." George owned that company.

Several years ago my company was engaged to produce a high-impact media show for the visitors' center at SEV headquarters. When I met George, I was impressed! The walls and plants and draperies were impressed with George! He had the biggest, friendliest smile you can imagine and appeared to be one of those people who knew exactly what he wanted when he wanted it—a no-grass-growing-under-his-feet-type man.

After my work was finished, I lost track of George, but each time I passed a big red sign, I thought about him. Then one day someone asked, "Did you hear about George Volkert? Poor ol' George, he has leukemia ... doesn't look too good!" Somehow I couldn't imagine George slowing down, even for a freight train.

I prayed a prayer and sent a note. One day he called, and we talked for almost an hour. He was in a remission and was doing great.

"What do you make of it, George? Do you ever ask *Why me?*" I was curious about this dynamo of a businessman.

"Sure have." I could picture George rolling back in his executive chair and putting his feet on his big executive-size desk. "... but ya' know, Sue, I never thought *Why me?* when I got tackled in football and got the daylights knocked out of me. You don't go around sayin' *Why me?* when you're playin' for Georgia Tech, at least not out loud; and believe me you gotta have a whole different level of tolerance for pain when you're playin' for Georgia Tech. You get knocked down and you get hurt, but you don't stay down. You get up and play again."

"What'dja learn, George?" I asked.

"My priorities have changed. I'm enjoying my family more. And you know what really means a lot to me? I've heard from people I hadn't thought of in thirty-five years, people who followed my football career when I was younger. I learned that people care."

We chatted for awhile and, unlike our first meeting, were relaxed and laid back. There wasn't some urgency to single-handedly conquer the world in the next ten minutes on either of our parts. "One more thing, Sue," he said in his most philosophic voice, "I think about the Lord more, and I think when the Lord is ready to take us, He'll take us. I don't worry anymore about things I can't control."

It seems to me that the great cause and effect ratio present in most people who have experienced a brush with death is an awakening or renewing of the awareness of God's presence in their lives. If the desire for God's presence wasn't there in the first place, often there is a first-time experience of *finding* God. One person I know, a good ol' boy type who had cancer, expressed it well when he said, "I got religion, real fast and real good!"

It was certainly true for me. It's difficult for me to believe we are moving through life randomly, that it is luck or chance or that it's simply "written in the stars." It's equally hard for me to think that God created us and walked away.

During my year of chemotherapy, when I wasn't sure whether I would die, it became important for me to sort myth from truth in regard to my personal faith.

I came to see that God wasn't nearly as complicated as I had once thought Him to be—that other than keeping the Ten Commandments, there weren't a lot of rules. In fact, it became easy for me to think of God as a loving parent who sees the big picture, just as Wayne and I saw the big picture for our children when they were young and immature. It would have been tempting to keep them locked up in an environmental bubble like those used for children with no immune system. Instead, we made decisions we felt would keep them safe, and we made decisions we thought would teach them to be wise. There were always things they not only questioned but didn't have the capacity to understand.

Often bad things happened to our children that we didn't cause, yet we tried to use those negative things for their good. We spent a great deal of time and energy protecting them from bad things; yet some of their most painful experiences taught them the most valuable lessons.

I have no trouble at all believing that the heavenly Parent took a negative thing like cancer and used it for good. I learned a Bible verse at summer camp one year that said, "In all things God works for the good of those who love him" (Romans 8:28).

My painful experience taught me new things about my husband: first of all how much he loves me and that I can count on him to take care of me. In fact, I have no doubt he would fix me his cure-all tomato soup night after night till the end of time, if need be. I don't want him to know it, but one of the reasons I got well so quickly was that I was pretty tired of that soup!

Family history was preserved because of my life-threatening illness. The stack of photo albums gets higher, and stories are repeated over and over so as to burn them into the minds of my children, my brothers, and their families.

I've learned to nurture friendships. I've come to understand and care about the hurts of others and find time to visit and send cards, something I never did before.

When my problems slowed me down enough to let it sink in, I discovered that God was as close as I allowed Him to be. I could actually feel His presence. When my prayers didn't seem to be getting any higher than the ceiling fan, I realized my friends were there waiting to take over for me. They were praying *for* me. I began to count on those prayers and I began to respond to God's *nudges*—when He brought someone to my mind—to pray for others.

Having cancer and having to go through a year of treatment may not have been a *privilege*, and I wouldn't wish it to happen to anyone else, but it makes me stop and ask, "Why *not* me?" My perspective has changed on almost everything: family, friendship, reunions, my Christian faith, sunsets, and porpoise shows.

After realizing that God was *there* and that He wasn't as complicated as I'd thought, the next thing I discovered was that there are answers to life's dilemmas in Holy Scripture. Sometimes we aren't even aware they are there until we need them. I was a tape recorder that could be turned on and off; push my button and I could turn on the verse that speaks of "... the peace of God, which transcends all understanding" (Philippians 4:7). One day in a hospital room, the reality of those words sank in.

Two weeks before Bob Benson died, he was still managing, with Peggy's help, to get to the sink to shave, brush his teeth, and comb his hair. It was a chore. Bob was so weak that when Peggy got him in front of the mirror, she would have to brace him there with her body.

One day their eyes caught in the mirror, and tears came. "Bob, have you been talkin' to the Lord this morning?" Peggy said. Bob nodded. "Bob, did you ask Him, *Why you? Why us?*" Bob nodded again. "What did He say?"

"He said, 'Ah, Bob, when you get to the place where you'll know the answer, the question isn't going to matter.'"

The third thing I learned (I should have learned it long ago—it's just that it seemed so far down the road) is that life here on earth isn't the end. The reality has finally sunk in. Someday I'll arrive at that *place* Bob referred to. The Scripture I learned as a child, "today you will be with me in paradise" (Luke 23:43), has a deep and passionate meaning for me and is a concept that now seems like a possibility.

Singing the old gospel song, "There's Going to Be a Meeting in the Air," that we sang with my parents and sang again after Dana's wedding, creates in me a strangely appealing longing.

To me, the original party girl, it means that God is planning a wingdinger of a party, and I'll be there! There will be decorations, food, and a band—or at least the heavenly equivalent. There will be family and friends, and it will go on forever! There's something else I know. It will be *so beautiful!* My daddy saw it that day so long ago, and he told me it was so.

"When can I say I'm cured?" I asked my doctor. "Is ten years—fifteen—the magic number?"

"When you die of natural causes," he replied. Not *if*, but *when!*

Aunt Annie said it best: "It'll get you. Sure as shootin', it'll get you!"

Even as I frantically shuffled through the family keepsakes at the time of Mother's death and tried to connect with the ancestors that shaped my life, I knew *beyond the shadow of a doubt* that someday I would join them in death, and that soon after, the signposts of my own life on earth would be reduced to a scrapbook, a few keepsakes, and a brass box full of pictures.

I *will* die. Someday I may get a bad report that cancer cells have once again invaded my body. Perhaps I'll be hit by a car or die of "natural causes." When that day comes, I can wholeheartedly say, "Let the party begin!"

> I used to think
> loving life so greatly
> that to die would be like
> leaving the party before the end.
> But now I know that the party is really happening
> somewhere else,
> that the light and the music escaping in snatches

to make the pulse beat faster and the tempo quicken
comes from another place.
And I know too
that when I get there,
the music and the love and the praise
will belong to Him,
and the music will never end.

—Author Unknown
(and may already be at the party!)

Afterword

I've PROMISED my FRIENDS at the American Cancer Society and the National Cancer Institute that whenever I speak or write, I'll call attention to breast health. Because I'm a video producer, I'm always looking for a new way to tell an old story. I've used rap music to introduce a new product, for a training film, and for the finale at a large convention. Clap your hands to an imaginary drumbeat, *think mean*, and read.

This rap's about a subject not often discussed
Self-breast examination, you know it's a must!
You bettah listen to us, we're here to crusade
We're the breast self-examination brigade.
What are our credentials? Why're we campaignin'?
Well, we've all had cancer, so we know what we're sayin'.
We're gonna tell you the facts. We're gonna tell you
    the rules
So listen real close now. Don't be fools!
Ready?
When you're in the shower or the tub
Make this routine a part of your scrub.
Lather your hands and examine your breasts
With soap on your hands you can feel them best.
Now stand before the mirror. Don't rush!
Get acquainted with your body. Don't blush!
First arms at your side; then high in the air
Make sure there are no discrepancies there.
Then raise your arms horizontally,
Check yourself for a visual abnormality.
Ch-ch-check yourself for abnormality!
Next lie on your back, left hand behind your head.

Use your right hand to check with fingers outspread.
(Use a circular motion, a c-c-circular motion.)
You're looking for lumps that might be hid.
Now using your left hand, repeat what you just did
(with a circular motion, a c-c-circular motion).
Take care of your body, it's the only one you got.
Have regular mammograms; stay close to your doc!
Till we can put cancer in the past tense
You gotta go usin' a little bit'a horse sense.
So be wise, be intelligent, be realistic.
Just follow these rules. Don't be a statistic.
Follow these rules. D-D-D-Don't be a statistic!
Copyright © 1993 Sue Buchanan